WIDER WORLD

SECOND EDITION

3

CONTENTS

Unit 0	Welcome to New Park	2
Unit 1	Tech check	6
Unit 2	Wild and beautiful	16
Unit 3	Tasty treats	26
Reading Time 1	Sharks	36
Unit 4	Entertain us!	38
Unit 5	To the limit	48
Unit 6	Explore more	58
Reading Time 2	The Railway Children	68
Unit 7	People power	70
Unit 8	Just justice	80
Unit 9	Lessons in life	90
Reading Time 3	The Professor	100
Exam Time 1	Units 1–3	102
Exam Time 2	Units 1–6	105
Exam Time 3	Units 1–9	108
Self-checks answer key		111

Welcome to New Park

VOCABULARY
Activities and interests | Home and furniture | Jobs | Everyday activities | Clothes and accessories | Countries and languages

GRAMMAR
There is/are with *some/any* | Possessive adjectives and possessive *'s* | Present Simple with adverbs of frequency | Present Continuous | *Was/were*, *there was/were* | Past Simple: regular verbs

0

0.1 Activities and interests | Home and furniture | *There is/are* with *some/any* | Possessive adjectives and possessive *'s*

GRAMMAR A — *There is/are* with *some/any*

Singular	Plural
+ There's a bed.	There are some books.
− There isn't a desk.	There aren't any mirrors.
? Is there a table?	Are there any chairs?

GRAMMAR B — Possessive adjectives and possessive *'s*

's = singular	Bea's mother is my dad's sister.
s' = plural	My friends' homes are near my house.
Possessive adjectives	my/your/his/her/its/our/their bedroom

1 🔊 0.1 Listen to Simon telling his friend Rob about his house. Tick (✓) the rooms and furniture they mention.

☐ bathroom   ☐ cupboard   ☐ kitchen
☐ bedroom   ☐ floor   ☐ mirror
☐ ceiling   ☐ garage

2 🔊 0.1 Listen again and choose the correct answer.
1 Simon's ___ is large.
 a bedroom   b bathroom
 c kitchen
2 Simon's dad likes ___.
 a taking photos   b reading books
 c listening to music
3 Simon's sister ___ when she does her hair.
 a makes a lot of noise   b sits on her bed
 c stands on the floor
4 Simon and Rob like ___.
 a listening to music   b taking photos
 c playing computer games

3 Match 1–5 with a–e to make sentences.
1 [c] We love going   a computer games.
2 [ ] All my friends like playing   b books.
3 [ ] Do you like listening   c to the cinema.
4 [ ] I don't like reading   d family photos.
5 [ ] My dad likes taking   e to music?

4 Complete the sentences with the words below. There are two extra words.

| can | can't | don't | likes | ~~love~~ | mind | stand |

1 I *love* going shopping with my friends, especially when I have money.
2 My brother _____ stand walking to school. He always gets the bus.
3 I don't _____ helping my sister with her homework. It's quite easy.
4 Jake _____ watching films at home, but I prefer going to the cinema.
5 I can't _____ waiting for people. It really annoys me!

5 Write the correct word for each definition.
1 You sit in this to wash yourself. b *a t h*
2 You lie on this to sleep. b_ _
3 This is made of glass, so you can see through it. w_ _ _ _ _
4 You can sit outside here when the weather is nice. g_ _ _ _ _
5 This has a door and you can keep things inside it. c_ _ _ _ _ _ _

6 Choose the correct option.
1 (*There's*) / *There are* a big table in the kitchen.
2 *There's* / *There are* lots of clothes on the floor in my bedroom.
3 There are *some* / *any* lovely flowers here.
4 There aren't *some* / *any* towels.
5 There *isn't* / *aren't* a mirror in the dining room.
6 *Are there* / *There are* any books in there?

7 Use the word in brackets to complete the sentences with a possessive adjective or the possessive *'s*.
1 These are *Jack's* shoes. (Jack)
2 This is _____ car. (my parents)
3 Is this _____ bag? (you)
4 This is _____ garden. (we)
5 That is _____ bike. (my brother)

Unit 0 2

0.2 Present Simple with adverbs of frequency | Jobs | Everyday activities

GRAMMAR — Present Simple with adverbs of frequency

+	−
I live in a small town. She works in a school.	I don't live in a big city. She doesn't teach Maths.

?	
Do you read a lot? Does she get up early?	Yes, I do./No, I don't. Yes, she does./No, she doesn't.

Always, usually, often, sometimes and *never* go before most verbs but after the verb *to be*.
I usually get up early. I'm never late for school.

1 Look at pictures A–F and write the jobs.

A — chef

B — _____

C — _____

D — _____

E — _____

F — _____

2 Order the words to make sentences.
1 usually / lunch / have / I / at one o'clock
   I usually have lunch at one o'clock.
2 always / late / Martha / is
3 go / I / to school / sometimes / by bus
4 Sara / often / tired / is
5 never / Paul / his homework / does
6 cooks / dinner / my dad / usually / for the family

3 Read the dialogue. Choose the correct option.
Sam: Where ¹you live /(do you live), Liam?
Liam: I ²live / lives in the city centre. My dad ³work / works in a bank.
Sam: ⁴Do / Does your mum have a job too?
Liam: Yes, she ⁵do / does. She's a teacher, but she ⁶not work / doesn't work every day. Both my parents work in the city centre.
Sam: And do your mum and dad ⁷take / takes you to school by car?
Liam: No, they ⁸don't / doesn't. I go on foot.

4 **WORD FRIENDS** Choose the correct answer.
1 I usually ____ my homework after dinner.
   a have   (b) do   c get
2 Do you ____ every morning?
   a have dinner b get home c have a shower
3 When do you usually ____ your friends?
   a see   b go out   c have
4 I often ____ up late at the weekend.
   a go   b get   c get home
5 We always ____ dinner at eight o'clock.
   a go   b have   c get up
6 We don't ____ school at the weekend.
   a go   b go at   c go to

5 🔊 0.2 Listen to Stacey describing her typical day. Mark the sentences T (true) or F (false).
1 ☐ Stacey doesn't have breakfast on school days.
2 ☐ Her mum is a doctor.
3 ☐ Stacey sometimes walks to school.
4 ☐ She doesn't like walking to school.
5 ☐ She does her homework late in the evening.
6 ☐ At the weekend Stacey usually sees Kyra.

3 Unit 0

0.3 Clothes and accessories | Present Continuous

GRAMMAR Present Continuous

+	−
I'm wearing a watch.	I'm not wearing a cap.
He's watching TV.	He isn't watching a film.
They're staying with us.	They aren't staying in the UK.

?	
Are you feeling relaxed?	Yes, I am./No, I'm not.
Is she wearing a skirt?	Yes, she is./No, she isn't.

1 Look at pictures A–F and write the words.

A _jacket_
B _____
C _____
D _____
E _____
F _____

2 Complete the sentences with the Present Continuous form of the verbs in brackets.
1. Carla _is having_ (have) a shower at the moment. Can you call back in ten minutes?
2. I can't talk to you now. I _____ (do) my homework.
3. _____ (your sisters/visit) their friends in London this weekend?
4. Tony and I _____ (not wear) our school uniforms today because it's Saturday.
5. Martin _____ (not play) football at the moment. _____ (he/watch) TV?
6. My parents _____ (not work) today. They _____ (sit) in the garden. They _____ (have fun)!

3 Read the dialogues. Choose the correct option.
1. A: Hi, Matt. What (are you doing) / are you do?
   B: I'm playing / I playing a computer game, but I don't doing / I'm not doing very well. It's really difficult.
2. A: Hi, Laura. Where's Mark? Is he / He is sleeping?
   B: No, he aren't / isn't. He's watches / watching a film in his bedroom.
3. A: Are / Do you feeling better today, Cara?
   B: Yes, I do / am, thanks. I feeling / I'm feeling much better.

4 How is each person feeling? Choose the correct answer.

> It's the first day of my holiday! The weather's lovely and I want to do lots of different things.

1. a frightened (b) excited c nervous

> All my friends are away this weekend. It's raining outside and there's nothing to do!

2. a bored b nervous c excited

> I don't like it when my sister wears my clothes. She never asks me first!

3. a excited b relaxed c annoyed

> I've got a Maths test tomorrow. The tests are always really difficult, so I never do very well.

4. a nervous b tired c relaxed

> I always go to bed late, so I never get much sleep. I want to sleep now!

5. a excited b bored c tired

> It's Saturday morning and I haven't got any homework this weekend! I'm watching TV.

6. a relaxed b frightened c annoyed

Unit 0

0.4 Countries and languages | Was/were | There was/were | Past Simple: regular verbs

GRAMMAR A — Was/were, there was/were

+	−
She was on holiday.	She wasn't on holiday.
We were on holiday.	We weren't on holiday.
There was a party.	There wasn't a party.
There were lots of people.	There weren't lots of people.

?	
Was it fun?	Yes, it was./No, it wasn't.
Were they at home?	Yes, they were./No, they weren't.
Was there a party?	Yes, there was./No, there wasn't.
Were there many people?	Yes, there were./No, there weren't.

1 Choose the correct option.

I really like my ¹*France / French* class at my language school. It's very interesting because there are people in it from all over the world. I'm ²*Portugal / Portuguese*, and my friend Jacek is from ³*Poland / Polish*. Then there are two girls who speak ⁴*Germany / German*: Lena and Mila. Ana sits opposite me and she's from ⁵*Italy / Italian*. There's also Deniz who is from ⁶*Turkey / Turkish* and Maria who is ⁷*Spain / Spanish*. We all have a lot of fun learning English. My parents want us to visit Asia, so I'm taking another class to learn ⁸*China / Chinese* next year!

2 Choose the correct answer.
1 ____ lots of people at the party last night – more than fifty!
   a Were   b There were   c There was
2 Jamie ____ at school yesterday.
   a wasn't   b were   c weren't
3 Our exams ____ very difficult last term.
   a was   b there weren't   c were
4 ____ the weather good last weekend?
   a Were   b Was there   c Was
5 ____ many people in the restaurant last night.
   a There wasn't   b There weren't
   c Weren't
6 ____ a good film on at the cinema last night?
   a Was there   b There wasn't
   c Were there

GRAMMAR B — Past Simple: regular verbs

+	−
She lived in Rio.	They didn't invite him.

?	
Did they like the film?	Yes, they did./No, they didn't.

3 Write the Past Simple forms of the verbs.
1 work   *worked*   6 enjoy ____
2 cook   ____   7 study ____
3 like   ____   8 play ____
4 live   ____   9 stop ____
5 try   ____   10 plan ____

4 Complete the sentences with the Past Simple form of the verbs below.

| live | ~~not enjoy~~ | not play | not rain | study | want |

1 I *didn't enjoy* the concert last weekend – it was terrible!
2 My parents ____ in a big house in New York when they were younger.
3 Alex ____ football yesterday because he was ill.
4 My mum ____ French at university.
5 My uncle ____ to be a pop singer when he was younger.
6 We were lucky because it ____ when we were on holiday.

5 Order the words to make questions.
1 you / like / your birthday presents / did / ?
   Did you like your birthday presents?
2 your parents / help / you / did / with your homework / ?
   _____
3 she / invite / all her friends / did / to the party / ?
   _____
4 cinema / what / the / at / you / did / watch / ?
   _____
5 you / work / hard / did / last term / ?
   _____
6 New York / did / when / visit / you / ?
   _____

5 Unit 0

Tech check

VOCABULARY
Technology | Using technology | Social media | Opposites | Time

GRAMMAR
Present Simple and Present Continuous, state verbs | Verb + -ing, verb + to-infinitive

1   1.1 Vocabulary
Lifestyle

1 ● Look at photos 1–7 and complete the words.

1 c _h a r g i n g_
  c _a b l e_

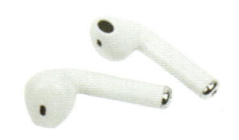

2 w _ _ _ _ _ _ _
  e _ _ _ _ _ _ _

3 p _ _ _ _ _ _ _
  a _ _ _

4 p _ _ _ _ _
  b _ _ _ _

5 r _ _ _ _ _ _
  c _ _ _ _ _ _ _

6 s _ _ _ _ _ _
  s _ _ _ _ _ _

7 w _ -f _   r _ _ _ _ _

2 ●● Write the correct word for each definition. Use words from Exercise 1.
1 You use this to change the channel on TV. _remote control_
2 You use this to remember your login information. _____
3 You use these to listen to music so that no one else can hear, but you don't need wires. _____
4 You use this to put more power into your phone from a wall socket. _____
5 You use this to connect to the internet. _____
6 A device you talk to. It can answer your questions and find information. _____
7 A gadget you can take anywhere to charge your phone. _____

3 ● **WORD FRIENDS** Choose the correct option.
1 (send) / connect a link
2 take / connect a screenshot
3 upload / set a new password
4 go / share a link
5 connect / set to the wi-fi router
6 take / search for information online
7 upload / set pictures

4 ●● Complete the sentences with the words below.

| password   ~~router~~   screenshot   search |
| send   upload |

1 This wi-fi _router_ doesn't work. Can you help me?
2 I always _____ for information safely when I'm doing a school project.
3 I _____ photos to my profile every day.
4 Can you _____ me the link again? I want to show it to my sister.
5 We set a new _____ every month.
6 First, take a _____ and then send it to Rose.

5 WORD FRIENDS Match the sentence halves.

1. d I don't post
2. ☐ She updates
3. ☐ Some people delete
4. ☐ Let's take
5. ☐ I follow
6. ☐ My mum wants to connect
7. ☐ I can only chat
8. ☐ Please don't add
9. ☐ Who do you message

a a selfie so we remember this moment!
b with friends at the weekend. Not after school.
c photos of themselves, but I don't mind.
d on social media every day.
e me to any more groups!
f her story when she does something fun.
g all my classmates on social media.
h when you can't do your homework?
i with me on social media!

6 Find nine technology verbs in the word search and write them below. Look →, ↓, ↗ and ↘.

N	J	V	U	Z	S	F	D	T	I	E	K
C	O	E	Y	J	W	J	E	L	T	S	M
U	O	H	R	H	U	G	L	H	X	E	X
P	F	N	U	W	A	W	E	I	Y	Y	M
D	S	U	N	S	O	K	T	B	S	G	K
A	Z	X	S	E	S	Z	E	L	G	H	V
T	M	E	W	D	C	P	O	S	T	M	W
E	M	M	V	L	Z	T	A	N	Z	F	S
X	E	C	T	E	T	A	K	E	U	Y	S
W	I	F	H	S	X	T	V	O	S	G	Z
S	I	R	N	A	T	H	A	D	D	H	Z
F	O	U	Q	B	T	F	O	L	L	O	W

1. post
2. _____
3. _____
4. _____
5. _____
6. _____
7. _____
8. _____
9. _____

7 Choose the correct answer.

1. My best friend always ___ selfies. He loves it.
   a makes   b takes   c follows
2. I want to ___ my sister to the group, but I don't know how.
   a add   b message   c delete
3. How often do you ___ something on social media?
   a connect   b post   c chat
4. My sister ___ with her friends every evening.
   a posts   b takes   c chats
5. I only ___ my story when something exciting happens.
   a add   b update   c delete
6. Please ___ that post. I don't like the photo!
   a follow   b take   c delete
7. When I make a new friend, I usually ___ with them on social media.
   a connect   b follow   c add
8. I ___ lots of famous athletes on social media.
   a connect   b update   c follow
9. My friend ___ me when she needs help with her homework.
   a messages   b connects   c chats

8 Complete the online profile with one word in each gap.

ELLA HOPKINS

About me

I love technology. Today in my bag I have my wireless ¹*earbuds*, so I can listen to music, my power ²_____ and of course my smartphone. I use it all the time to ³_____ for information and to ⁴_____ with my friends. Sometimes I take ⁵_____ and post the nice photos on ⁶_____ media. I don't update my ⁷_____ very often because at the moment I go to school every day and nothing exciting happens. I ⁸_____ all my favourite singers on social media, but I don't play games. My sister only goes online to play games. She never ⁹_____ pictures or messages her friends. I think she's crazy!

I can talk about everyday technology.

1.2 Grammar

Present Simple and Present Continuous, state verbs

GRAMMAR — Present Simple and Present Continuous, state verbs

Present Simple
They usually *travel* on a tour bus.
She *doesn't write* the blog every day.
Do they *speak* English? Yes, they *do*.

Present Continuous
He*'s travelling* a lot these days.
They *aren't recording* a song at the moment.
Is he *skateboarding* now? No, he *isn't*.

State verbs
Some verbs don't normally have a continuous form:
love, like, hate, know, think, see, feel, understand, want, need

1 ● Match questions 1–6 with answers a–f.
1. [c] Are you enjoying the film?
2. [ ] Does your uncle live in London?
3. [ ] Do you search for information online every day?
4. [ ] Are they making a film?
5. [ ] Is Jack practising on his skateboard?
6. [ ] Do your friends play in a band?

a No. I only search for information online when I do my homework.
b No, they aren't. They're just taking some selfies.
c ~~Yes, I am. It's brilliant!~~
d Yes, they do, and they're awesome!
e No, he isn't. He's playing tennis.
f No, he doesn't. He lives in Manchester.

2 ● Complete the sentences with the Present Simple form of the verbs below.

| feel | ~~know~~ | not think | not understand | want |

1. I *know* Kate very well – she's my best friend.
2. I'm going home because I _____ ill.
3. I _____ what you're saying. Can you repeat it, please?
4. My brother _____ to buy a new smartphone.
5. I _____ she's from France, but she's got a French name.

3 ●● Complete the sentences with the Present Simple or Present Continuous form of the verbs in brackets.

1. I *usually post* (usually/post) on social media every day, but today I _____ (not upload) anything.
2. Jez _____ (learn) the guitar at the moment because he _____ (want) to be in a band.
3. I _____ (try) to connect with Anna now because I _____ (need) to speak to her.
4. We _____ (usually/cycle) to school, but it _____ (rain) today, so we _____ (go) by bus.
5. I _____ (look) for my charging cable. I _____ (not know) where I left it.

4 ●● Read the dialogues. Choose the correct option.
1. A: Hi. What *(are you doing)* / *do you do*?
   B: *I try* / *I'm trying* to take a selfie while I'm on my skateboard, but *I think* / *I'm thinking* it's impossible!
2. A: *Do you like* / *Are you liking* the new game?
   B: Yes, *I am* / *do*. But *I don't spend* / *I'm not spending* much time on computer games at the moment because *I work* / *I'm working* hard for my exams.
3. A: Hi! Are those your new wireless earbuds? What *do you listen* / *are you listening* to?
   B: That new band, The Feds. *Do you know* / *Are you knowing* them?

5 ●●● Complete the email with the Present Simple or Present Continuous form of the verbs in brackets.

Hi Jackie,

How are you? I ¹*'m staying* (stay) with my uncle in Birmingham this weekend because there's a big technology show here. My uncle ² _____ (come) to this event every year. This year he ³ _____ (want) to buy a smart speaker. You ⁴ _____ (know) I ⁵ _____ (love) technology, so this is a great place for me. I want to get new wireless earbuds. By the way, do you like Alvaro Soler? Right now I ⁶ _____ (download) his latest album. His music is fantastic!
What ⁷ _____ (you/do) this weekend? Write and tell me.

Paul

Unit 1 | 8 | I can use different tenses to talk about the present.

On the Portal
Extra Practice Activities: Lesson 1.2

1.3 Reading and Vocabulary
Science competitions and projects

1 Read the texts quickly and answer the questions.
1 Who likes writing quizzes?
_____
2 Who is looking for a team mate?
_____

Text 1

Win a place at Coding Camp!
Do you love Science and Technology? I need you!

Every year there is a technology competition for young people aged 11–16. Teams have to design an original quiz app. The prize is always excellent, for example smart speakers. This year, the prize is a place at a coding summer camp. It lasts one week, you learn about coding and make a robot. There can be two to four people on each team. Message me and we can chat.

Jemima

Text 2

Hi Jemima,

My name's Yuan. The coding competition looks really fun. I want to enter. I have some clever ideas for the quiz. In my free time I often make up quizzes to post on social media. I don't know very much about designing apps and it doesn't look easy. However, I'm searching for information online right now. There are some cool websites about it. By the way, I'm in the same Maths class as you. I sit next to the boy with red hair! Let's talk after the next lesson.

Yuan

Hi Yuan,

That sounds great! I am learning about apps in computer class and it's not very complicated. I'm working on a password app now. But I'm not very good at quizzes. What topics do you think are best? Do you have any favourite quiz apps I can download on my new smartphone? Oh! I'm in a group about coding. I'm adding you right now.

See you,
Jemima

I can understand a message and an email about Science competitions and projects.

2 Read the texts again and answer the questions.

Text 1
1 Who is looking for a team?
_____
2 Who can enter the competition?
_____
3 How long is the coding camp?
_____
4 How many people can be on each team?
_____

Text 2
1 Who likes writing quiz questions?
_____
2 What lesson do Jemima and Yuan have together?
_____
3 What is Jemima studying in computer class?
_____
4 Who has a new smartphone?
_____

3 Order the letters to complete the words.
1 We need new ideas: we need something fresh and o_riginal_ (ALOGINIR).
2 My brother is so c_____ (VECLER). He can learn anything.
3 I like being different. I sometimes wear s_____ (GRANEST) clothes.
4 I heard that this film is e_____ (LEXENCELT). Let's watch it tomorrow.
5 Maths is a c_____ (PAOETLCCMID) subject, but I'm quite good at it.
6 Gina builds s_____ (ASEF) homes for bats.
7 I don't like this book. It's really b_____ (OBNIGR).
8 Let's not go out! The weather is t_____ (LEBERTRI) today. It's too windy.
9 Our Chemistry teacher always tells us to be careful during experiments. Sometimes they may be d_____ (AGSDUEONR).
10 I found some really c_____ (LOOC) apps that can help us with our project!
11 It wasn't clever at all! It was rather s_____ (UTDIPS).

1.4 Grammar
Verb + -ing, verb + to-infinitive

GRAMMAR Verb + -ing, verb + to-infinitive

Verb + -ing
After: *avoid, can't stand, enjoy, finish, look forward to, (not) mind, miss, practise, stop;* after prepositions
I *don't mind seeing* your room.
She is tired *after driving* the whole night.

Verb + to-infinitive
After: *agree, allow, ask, choose, decide, forget, hope, learn, need, offer, plan, remember, try, want, would like/love*
I'm *trying to talk* to Abe.

Verb + ing or to-infinitive
After: *like, love, hate, prefer, start*
Do you *prefer seeing/to see* the beach?

1 ● Order the words to make sentences.
1 enjoy / with / chatting / I / online / friends
   I enjoy chatting with friends online.
2 forget / sometimes / to / do / I / my homework
   _____
3 hoping / he's / pass / his exams / to
   _____
4 misses / seeing / she / her cousins
   _____
5 I / love / to / would / come / to the party
   _____
6 always / he / his room / cleaning / avoids
   _____

2 ● Match the sentence halves.
1 [c] I'm looking forward
2 [   ] Sonia can't
3 [   ] I don't
4 [   ] I would like
5 [   ] Dan is very good
6 [   ] Please stop

a mind helping with the party.
b making so much noise!
c ~~to seeing you.~~
d at playing the guitar.
e to go to New York.
f stand cooking.

3 ●● Complete the sentences with the correct form of the verbs in brackets.
1 My grandma is trying *to learn* (learn) how to upload pictures.
2 Why don't you come to my house when you finish _____ (do) your homework?
3 We're planning _____ (buy) a smart speaker.
4 Are you interested in _____ (see) the new Marvel film?
5 Mark never offers _____ (do) the washing-up!
6 My sister sometimes asks me _____ (help) her with her homework.

4 ●● Choose the correct option.
1 My brother often chooses (*to watch*) / *watching* films on his tablet.
2 I can't stand *to listen* / *listening* to that strange music!
3 Hurry up – we need *to be* / *being* on time!
4 I hope my dad agrees *to pay* / *paying* for a waterproof camera.
5 I need *to take* / *taking* a screenshot so I don't forget this information.

5 ●●● Complete the text with the correct form of the verbs below.

| come | cook | give | ~~make~~ | meet |
| organise | see | send | talk | visit |

I love ¹*making* video calls on my new smartphone. My best friend lives in a different city, so we try ² _____ once a week. Next month it's her birthday, and I'm planning ³ _____ an online party for her. I've asked all our friends ⁴ _____. I'm quite good at ⁵ _____, but I don't think a cake is a good idea for an online meeting! We also message each other every day. We enjoy ⁶ _____ each other selfies. I always look forward to ⁷ _____ her photos. They always make me smile.
I hope ⁸ _____ her hometown soon. I would like ⁹ _____ her new friends and see her new school. Also, an online party is great, but I'd love ¹⁰ _____ her a real hug right now!

Unit 1 | 10 | I can use verbs followed by the *-ing* form and/or the *to*-infinitive.

On the Portal
Extra Practice Activities: Lesson 1.4

1.5 Listening and Vocabulary
Are you technology crazy?

1 Choose the correct option.
1. I get up for school at 7 (a.m.) / p.m.
2. There are sixty seconds in *a minute* / *an hour*.
3. I often see my friends *in* / *at* the weekend.
4. I usually take a selfie *once* / *once time* a week.
5. We sit around the table *at* / *on* mealtimes.
6. I sometimes watch TV *in* / *on* the evening.

2 Match the sentence halves.
1. _f_ We have our lunch in the canteen
2. ___ The show is on TV three
3. ___ There are sixty seconds in one
4. ___ I sometimes feel tired in
5. ___ I only see my grandparents twice
6. ___ I sometimes go shopping on

a Saturdays.
b the afternoon.
c times a week.
d minute.
e a year.
f ~~at lunchtime.~~

3 🔊 1.1 **Listen to the first part of a radio programme. What is the programme about?**
a ☐ some people who are trying some new technology for a month
b ☐ some people who are not using technology for a month

4 🔊 1.2 Listen to the second part of the programme. Match people 1–5 with the activity they miss the most.

NAME		ACTIVITY
1 ☐	Isla	a following stars online
2 ☐	Lucy	b chatting to friends
3 ☐	Ben	c using the internet to do schoolwork
4 ☐	Sara	d writing blog posts
5 ☐	Jeremy	e listening to the latest music

5 🔊 1.3 Complete what Isla says with the words below. There are two extra words. Listen and check.

| evenings | hates | information | online |
| terrible | trying | usually | |

Well, I ¹_____ message my best friend Lucy in the ²_____, but of course, now I can't do that. She's doing the challenge too. For me it's OK because I see her at school, but she ³_____ it. The worst thing is trying to do homework. I can't go online to search for ⁴_____ and that's ⁵_____! Books are OK, but it's much slower without the internet.

I can understand a radio programme about using technology.

On the Portal
Extra Practice Activities: Lesson 1.5

1.6 Speaking
Problem-solving

1 🔊 **1.4** Listen and repeat the phrases.

SPEAKING — **Problem-solving**

Describing the problem
The internet is working, but it's slow.
Where do you think you plug it in?
The signal's really weak in here!

Suggesting solutions
We could upload the video to see if the router works.
Let's install it!
What about looking online?
Why don't we download one?
Shall we check the other rooms?

Accepting or rejecting solutions
(That's a) good/great idea.
Yes, let's give it a try.
You can't play video games outside!

2 Complete the dialogues with the words below.

| about | can't | could | idea | let's | shall |
| ~~think~~ | try | | | | |

1 A: Where do you *think* we should put the new wi-fi router?
   B: We _____ plug it in here.
2 A: What _____ looking online?
   B: That's a good _____.
3 A: _____ I turn it on now?
   B: Yes, let's give it a _____.
4 A: _____ take the television and games console into the garden.
   B: You _____ play video games outside!

3 Complete the sentences with the words below.

| about | could | don't | idea | ~~let's~~ | weak |

1 *Let's* try plugging it in.
2 We _____ look for a video with instructions online.
3 That's a stupid _____.
4 The 4G signal is really _____ in here!
5 Why _____ we ask Mum?
6 What _____ taking a screenshot?

4 Match suggestions 1–5 with responses a–e.
1 [c] Let's make a video about photography.
2 [   ] You could use the camera on your new phone.
3 [   ] Let's go into town now.
4 [   ] The internet's working, but it's really slow.
5 [   ] Shall I we put this smart speaker on the garden table?

a Good idea. I can try it out for the first time.
b We could move the wi-fi router to the kitchen.
c ~~Great idea! We're both really good at taking photos!~~
d You can't use it outside. It will get wet.
e Why not? We can meet some friends there.

5 🔊 **1.5** Complete the dialogue with sentences a–e. Listen and check.

Joe: Right, we need to upload a cover photo for our new travel blog. What's the best idea?
Ann: ¹c
Joe: Hmm, I'm not sure. I'm not smiling in that picture. I'd rather delete it.
Ann: OK. Well, shall we use this one from the concert in Spain?
Joe: ² ____
Ann: OK, we've got the photo. We could write the profile now.
Joe: ³ ____
Ann: Great! Let's start by saying who we are and where we live.
Joe: ⁴ ____
Ann: You're right. I think we can say what our hobbies are instead.
Joe: ⁵ ____ You can write about drawing and I can say something about horse-riding.
Ann: Great! Let's do that!

a Yes, let's give it a try. I've got some good ideas to make it interesting.
b You can't say where you live online. It's not safe.
c ~~What about the photo of us on the beach?~~
d That's a great idea. I'm sending the link now.
e That's true.

I can describe a problem, suggest solutions and respond to suggestions.

1.7 Writing

A description of your daily routine and online hobbies

1 Read the article. Match paragraphs 1–3 with topics a–c below.

a ☐ being a different person online
b ☐ a typical day
c ☐ knowing the difference between a virtual life and real life

My life in the **real world** and **online**   by Matt Thompson

1 Like most teenagers, I love going online and chatting to friends, **but** I also have my real life. On a normal day I go to school and I often meet my friends in the afternoon. We like going to the cinema or a café. At the moment, we're studying a lot **because** we have exams soon. Revising for exams is a bit boring. In the evenings, I finish my homework and then I update my story on social media.

2 At the weekend, I always have free time, **so** I visit my favourite virtual world. You make an avatar **as well as** choose a place to live. You can do anything! At the moment, I'm a chef in a restaurant in Italy. It's fun. It can be stressful **too**. Sometimes the customers are unhappy, just like in real life!

3 **Although** I enjoy my online world, I know it's not real. The time I spend in the real world with my friends is more important. **However**, my virtual world helps me relax when life is complicated. So I always look forward to spending time there **as well**.

2 Read the article again. Mark the sentences T (true) or F (false).

1 ☐ Matt and his friends enjoy spending time together.
2 ☐ Matt is studying for exams at school.
3 ☐ Matt wants to be a chef in the future.
4 ☐ Matt's virtual world is more important to him than the real world.

3 Choose the correct option.

1 My virtual world isn't very big. *Although /* (*However*), I enjoy spending time in it.
2 I meet lots of interesting people, *so / because* I never get bored.
3 I play on my laptop *as well as / as well on* my smartphone.
4 There's a theme park here and a zoo *but / too*.

4 Complete Anna's notes with the words below.

friends   hours   online   school   ~~sister~~
smartphone   tennis   weekend

Daily routine
- mum, dad and ¹ *sister*
- enjoy going to ² _____ – love Art class
- favourite hobbies are ³ _____ and photography

Online hobbies
- lives a virtual life on an island
- usually play at the ⁴ _____ or after school
- play on my ⁵ _____
- enjoy having lots of ⁶ _____ friends

How I combine these worlds
- I don't spend more than a couple of ⁷ _____ online each week
- always make time for my real world, ⁸ _____ and hobbies

WRITING TIME

5 Imagine you are Anna. Write an article about your daily routine and online hobbies using the notes in Exercise 4.

1 Find ideas
Make notes about:
- your daily routine and online hobbies.
- how you can combine your daily routine with your online hobbies.

2 Plan and write
- Organise your ideas into paragraphs. Use Matt's article to help you.
- Write a draft article.

3 Check
- Check language: did you use connectors correctly?
- Check grammar: did you mostly use the Present Simple and adverbs of frequency?
- Write the final version of your article.

I can write a description of my daily routine and online hobbies.

My Language File

WORDLIST 🔊 1.6

Technology
charging cable (n) _____
password app (n) _____
power bank (n) _____
remote control (n) _____
smart speaker (n) _____
wi-fi router (n) _____
wireless earbuds (n) _____

Word friends (using technology)
connect to the wi-fi router _____
search for information online _____
send a link _____
set a new password _____
share a link _____
take a screenshot _____
upload pictures _____

Word friends (social media)
add someone to a group _____
chat with friends _____
connect with someone on social media _____
delete a photo _____
delete a post _____
follow someone on social media _____
message someone _____
post on social media _____
take a selfie _____
update your story _____

Time
6 a.m./6 p.m. _____
at lunchtime _____
at mealtimes _____
at the weekend _____
hour (n) _____
in the afternoon _____
in the evening _____
in the morning _____
minute (n) _____
on a schoolday/Sunday(s) _____
once/twice/three times a day/ week/month/year _____
second (n) _____

Opposites
boring – cool, fun, interesting, original _____
dangerous – safe _____
easy – complicated _____
normal – strange _____
stupid – clever _____
terrible – excellent _____

Extra words
awesome (adj) _____
background (n) _____
blog (n) _____
catch up with (v) _____
channel (n) _____
charge (v) _____
choice (n) _____
choose (v) _____
command (v) _____
competition (n) _____
effect (n) _____
essential (adj) _____
gadget (n) _____
helpful (adj) _____
icon (n) _____
impression (n) _____
install (v) _____
live in concert _____
look for (v) _____
luckily (adv) _____
microphone (n) _____
participant (n) _____
perform (v) _____
plug in (v) _____
popular (adj) _____
practise (v) _____
pretty (= quite) (adv) _____
recipe (n) _____
record a song _____
robot (n) _____
Science project (n) _____
set up (v) _____
signal (n) _____
sound (n) _____
study (n) _____
style (n) _____
switch on/off (v) _____
take place _____
tech answer (n) _____
tell a joke _____
trick (n) _____
video call (n) _____
virtual world (n) _____
vlog (n) _____
voice assistant (n) _____
youth group (n) _____

Sounds good!
Come on!
Not out there!

MY LANGUAGE NOTES

My favourite words/expressions from this unit

Self-check

Vocabulary

1 Complete the words in the sentences.
1. My phone has no power – I need to find my c_ _ _ _ _ _ _ _ _ _ c_ _ _ _ _ _.
2. Let's t_ _ _ a s_ _ _ _ _ _ and send it to Mum. She loves seeing photos of us together.
3. Do you usually u_ _ _ _ _ _ _ pictures to your social media profile?
4. I love listening to music, so I'm excited about my new w_ _ _ _ _ _ _ _ e_ _ _ _ _.
5. Oh no! I deleted the p_ _ _ _.
6. He's sharing the l_ _ _ _ to a website about the museum right now.
7. The r_ _ _ _ _ _ _ control isn't working, so we can't watch TV!
8. Who is your favourite star to f_ _ _ _ _ _ on social media?
9. Can you a_ _ _ me to the g_ _ _ _ so we can share photos?
10. Do you know how to t_ _ _ _ _ a s_ _ _ _ _ _ _ _ _ _ so we can save this information?

2 Choose the correct answer.
1. Smart speakers are a(n) ____ idea, but I don't want one.
   a complicated b original c normal
2. I hate this photo! Please ____ it.
   a post b delete c follow
3. How can I ____ to the wi-fi router?
   a connect b set c chat
4. Send me a ____ to that article, please.
   a link b message c post
5. I don't like that film. I think it's ____
   a fun b cool c terrible

3 Complete the sentences with the words below. There is one extra word.

> day evening mealtimes minute twice weekend

1. I go swimming _____ a week, on Wednesdays and Fridays.
2. I always read a book in the _____ before bed.
3. Wait a _____. I just have to get my phone.
4. What time do you get up on a school _____?
5. I'm always very hungry at _____.

Grammar

4 Complete the sentences with the Present Simple or Present Continuous form of the verbs in brackets.
1. I _____ (chat) with my friends at the moment.
2. I _____ (not often/watch) films on my smartphone – I prefer a bigger screen.
3. My uncle _____ (live) near the beach.
4. I _____ (not like) her music.
5. It _____ (not rain) now, so we can go out.
6. _____ Jake _____ (want) to come too?
7. _____ you _____ (do) your homework right now?

5 Choose the correct option.
1. Hurry up – I can't stand *to be / being* late!
2. George never offers *to pay / paying* for anything.
3. Please be quiet – I'm trying *to connect / connecting* to the new wi-fi router.
4. My parents allow me *to stay up / staying up* late at the weekend.
5. It's OK – I don't mind *to help / helping* you.
6. Mike hopes *to buy / buying* a new speaker.
7. Remember *to delete / deleting* that photo.
8. My mum avoids *to go / going* online at the weekends.

Speaking

6 Complete the dialogue with one word in each gap.
A: [1]_____ we organise something for Alana's birthday?
B: Yes, great idea. We [2]_____ have a party.
A: I'm not sure. A party's quite expensive. [3]_____ don't we go for a pizza?
B: I'd rather [4]_____. I don't really like pizza.
A: OK, well, [5]_____ about a film night at my house?
B: Yes. That's a good idea. Let's do that.

YOUR SCORE

Vocabulary: __/20   Speaking: __/5
Grammar: __/15   Total: __/40

Wild and beautiful

2

VOCABULARY
Word building: weather | Weather and climate | Adverbs of degree | Camping | In the wild

GRAMMAR
Past Simple: regular and irregular verbs | Past Continuous and Past Simple

2.1 Vocabulary
Weather and climate

1 ● Complete the weather words.

Noun	Adjective
snow	¹s n o w y
²s __ __	sunny
fog	³f __ __ __
⁴c __ __ __ __	cloudy
wind	⁵w __ __ __
⁶i __ __	icy
storm	⁷s __ __ __ __
⁸r __ __ __	rainy

2 ●● Choose the correct answer.
1 We don't want to drive because it's ___ today, so you can't see very well.
   a ice   b wind   **c foggy**
2 We can't go out in our boat because it's ___ and the sea is rough.
   a cloud   b sunny   c stormy
3 It's very cold here in winter and there's often ___ on the ground.
   a snow   b windy   c rain
4 Look, it's a lovely ___ day. Let's go swimming in the sea!
   a icy   b sunny   c wind
5 You should drive slowly when there's ___ on the roads.
   a fog   b stormy   c ice
6 There's a lovely blue sky today – it isn't ___ at all.
   a cloudy   b sun   c snow
7 Sometimes things blow away when it's very ___.
   a icy   b windy   c rainy
8 Everything in the garden gets wet when it's ___.
   a cloud   b rainy   c sun

3 ●● Find and correct the mistakes in the sentences.
1 It's very fog today.
   It's very foggy today.
2 Oh no! It's getting cloud!
   _____
3 The sunny is beautiful today.
   _____
4 Look, it's snow. Let's build a snowman!
   _____
5 It's getting a bit storm now.
   _____

4 ● Complete the weather words.
1 h <u>u</u> r r i <u>c</u> <u>a</u> ne
2 dr __ __ g __ t
3 fl __ __ d
4 s __ ns __ __ ne
5 g __ l __
6 t __ u __ __ e __

5 ●● Complete the comments with the words below. There are two extra words.

| breeze | drought | flood | gale | hurricanes |
| lightning | shower | sunshine | ~~thunder~~ |

1 I love stormy weather, but my brother doesn't like *thunder* and _____.
2 I have an umbrella and it's only a _____. We won't get wet.
3 It's a lovely sunny day with a nice cool _____.
4 It's very windy, but we don't have _____ in my country.
5 We often have a _____ when it rains a lot and the river gets too high.
6 It's very hot this year, and it isn't raining. I hope there isn't a _____.

Unit 2   16

6 Order the letters and complete the words in the sentences.
1. The weather forecast in Florida is for s*trong* (ROSTNG) winds.
2. It will be m_____ (NIMUS) twelve degrees at the weekend.
3. The weather today is f_____ (ZERENFIG) cold. Wear a warm jacket.
4. The temperature is f_____ (LAFLGNI).
5. The weather today is f_____ (NIFE); warm and sunny!
6. My hometown has a hot c_____ (MALICTE).

7 WORD FRIENDS Choose the word that does NOT fit in each sentence.
1. The temperature is ____.
   a falling   b minus   c rising
2. The weather forecast is for ____ temperatures.
   a high   b low   c bad
3. It will be ____ today.
   a heavy   b warm   c dry
4. The area has a ____ climate.
   a cold   b mild   c strong
5. The weather forecast is for heavy ____.
   a wind   b snow   c rain
6. It will be ____.
   a cold climate   b 10 degrees   c boiling hot

8 Read what four people say about the weather in their area. Choose the correct option.

It will be wet today with ¹*showers* / fog here in Manchester, so you need your umbrella. The temperature is ² mild / falling, so you definitely need your coat too.

Sometimes we have ³ droughts / floods here and the water comes up to our front door. It's quite wet at the moment. I hope it stops ⁴ raining / rainy soon. It's quite a heavy ⁵ gale / shower!

Winters are usually ⁶ boiling / freezing cold where I live and we often have lots of ⁷ snow / snowy. It's great because we can build snowmen, but the roads are dangerous because they're often ⁸ cloudy / icy.

Usually the summers are warm and ⁹ minus / mild here, but this year it's ¹⁰ boiling / freezing hot. I'm going to the beach later!

I can talk about the weather and climate.

9 Complete the weather forecast with one word in each gap.

Weather around the world

MADRID
- In Madrid it's boiling ¹*hot* today and the sky is a lovely clear blue.

LONDON
- In London it's quite cold and it's also starting to get a bit ²_____, so hold on to your hats!

PARIS
- In Paris the weather forecast is for high ³_____, so remember to wear a sun hat.

TORONTO
- It's a cold night in Toronto, with ⁴_____ temperatures of around 0°C.

SYDNEY
- In Sydney the ⁵_____ continues. Plants are dying because it's so dry and everyone is hoping for some rain soon.

ROME
- In Rome it's a lovely sunny day, with a temperature of around 22 ⁶_____.

On the Portal
Extra Practice Activities: Lesson 2.1

2.2 Grammar

Past Simple: regular and irregular verbs

GRAMMAR — Past Simple: regular and irregular verbs

Regular verbs
It **looked** pinkish orange.
The storms **didn't move**.
When **did** that **happen**?

Irregular verbs
We **saw** an unusual storm.
I **didn't know** what to do.
Did you **take** any photos? Yes, I **did**./No, I **didn't**.

We use the Past Simple with past time expressions, e.g. *yesterday, last week/year; two hours/days/weeks/years ago, in April, in 1595.*

1 ● Match infinitives 1–5 with their Past Simple forms a–e.
1 c become   a took
2 ___ see   b thought
3 ___ know   c ~~became~~
4 ___ think   d knew
5 ___ take   e saw

2 ● Complete the sentences with the Past Simple form of the verbs in brackets.
1 I was tired and I *wanted* (want) to go home.
2 I _____ (not stay) inside when it rained. I got wet.
3 My dad _____ (study) Maths at university.
4 Ralph _____ (not help) us to organise the party last week.
5 I _____ (spot) Tim in the park yesterday.
6 Sara _____ (not look) very happy yesterday.

3 ●● Complete the sentences with the Past Simple form of the pairs of verbs below.

feel/make   get/not go   meet/not like
not take/go   ~~see/not know~~

1 We were scared when we *saw* the flood and we *didn't know* what to do.
2 Jake _____ many photos when he _____ to Canada last year.
3 The storm _____ quite bad, so we _____ outside.
4 I _____ really happy with the app that I _____ in the IT lesson.
5 She _____ George last year, but she _____ him at first.

4 ●● Complete the dialogues. Use the Past Simple.
1 A: Where *did you save* our presentation?
   B: I saved it in a new folder, on the desktop.
2 A: When _____?
   B: The hurricane happened on Tuesday night.
3 A: Where _____ your coat?
   B: I put it in the kitchen.
4 A: _____ any photos of the storm?
   B: No, I didn't take any photos.
5 A: When _____ to Paris?
   B: I moved to Paris last summer.

5 ●●● Complete the text with the Past Simple form of the verbs below.

become   feel   help   not sleep   not stop
not think   not want   ~~see~~   visit   watch

Wow! What amazing weather! ¹*Did* you *see* the snowstorm last night? It started at about eight o'clock, and at first I ² _____ it was very bad. But the snow soon ³ _____ quite thick on the ground. It ⁴ _____ snowing for about five hours! I ⁵ _____ at all because I ⁶ _____ so excited – I ⁷ _____ to miss anything! This morning some friends ⁸ _____ us at home and ⁹ _____ us to clear the snow away from our door. Thanks, guys! I don't know about the weather today. ¹⁰ _____ you _____ the weather forecast on TV this morning? What's the weather like where you are?

6 ●●● Complete the text with one word in each gap.

Yes, I ¹*saw* the snowstorm ² _____ night – amazing! The last storm like this was five years ³ _____. It ⁴ _____ place ⁵ _____ December, right at the beginning of the winter. We made some amazing snowmen that year, but unfortunately they ⁶ _____ last very long because the snow soon melted. I posted some photos yesterday, when the storm started. ⁷ _____ you see them?

On the Portal
Extra Practice Activities: Lesson 2.2

I can use the Past Simple to talk about past events.

2.3 Reading and Vocabulary
Life in a cold place

1 Match the sentence halves.
1. [b] Wow. She looks completely
2. [ ] I called the police about a really
3. [ ] It snowed all day. I'm quite
4. [ ] Last summer was absolutely
5. [ ] The climate here is very
6. [ ] I took some totally

a worried about walking home.
b different. Did she change her hairstyle?
c awesome photos of the lightning.
d boring. The weather is the same all year long.
e boiling. On some days it was over 40 degrees.
f strange man on our street.

2 Read the article. Tick (✓) the topics Takashi mentions.
- [ ] the weather
- [ ] taking photos
- [ ] skiing
- [ ] films
- [ ] homework
- [ ] pets

3 Read the article again and choose the correct answer.
1. Takashi says
   a he usually stays in bed when it snows.
   b the temperature in Sapporo is usually minus seven in winter.
   c his hometown usually has a lot of snow.
2. Last month Takashi
   a learned how to make chocolate.
   b visited a park with his friends.
   c went on holiday with his family.
3. When Takashi climbed a mountain, he didn't
   a take enough water.
   b have time to take photos.
   c want to climb in the dark.
4. Takashi says he feels good when he
   a remembers the day he climbed the mountain.
   b looks at the photos he took on the mountain.
   c spends time outside, climbing mountains.

My hometown is awesome!
Takashi lives in Sapporo in Northern Japan.

Do you like snowy weather? Sapporo – my hometown is famous for very heavy snow. When I woke up today, the temperature was minus seven degrees. I wanted to stay in bed, but my sister came and asked me to go skiing. I love skiing, so I quickly got dressed. Sometimes there is so much snow that I can't get to school. But it's not cold all year. In summer it can be warm and sunny. Perfect for trekking.

Sapporo is the fifth biggest city in Japan, and there are great places to visit. Last month I went to a chocolate factory with my family. We went on a tour and they showed us how they make chocolate. I tried some and it was totally delicious! Then we took a walk in one of many amazing parks in Sapporo.

There is a mountain close to my home called Moiwayama. Last summer I went on a trip there with my friends. It was absolutely boiling when we climbed the mountain, so it took a long time to reach the top. We rested and drank water every thirty minutes. I was quite worried when it started to get dark.

I didn't want to be on the mountain at night, but it was all OK in the end. We got back home when it was still light. The views from the top were amazing and I love looking at the photos I took. Thinking about that day makes me feel great. Every year in February there is a special event in Sapporo – the Snow Festival. It started more than seventy years ago, and now teams from more than twenty countries come to create sculptures. You can see sculptures made from snow and ice all around the city. Last year one team created a really amazing *Star Wars* sculpture. It was my favourite!

I can understand an article about life in a cold place.

2.4 Grammar
Past Continuous and Past Simple

GRAMMAR — Past Continuous and Past Simple

Past Continuous
It *was raining*.
We *weren't thinking* about the weather.
Were you *running*? Yes, I *was*./No, I *wasn't*.

Past Continuous and Past Simple
Abe *downloaded* his photo *while* his dad *was making* a warm drink.
He *was throwing* the frisbee *when* lightning *hit* a tree.

1 ● Complete the sentences with the Past Continuous form of the verbs in brackets.
1 He said the weather was too hot while he *was visiting* (visit) Mexico.
2 They _____ (not listen) when the weather forecast was on TV.
3 What _____ (you/do) when you saw the hurricane?
4 They _____ (swim) in the sea when the heavy rain started.
5 _____ (it/snow) when you left home?
6 Someone took my umbrella while I _____ (not look).

2 ● Choose the correct option.
1 I was running for the bus when I (*dropped*) / *was dropping* my phone.
2 Jack fell asleep while he *watched* / *was watching* the film.
3 We were walking home when the breeze *started* / *was starting* to get stronger.
4 There was a flood while my cousins *stayed* / *were staying* in Japan.
5 The bear *appeared* / *was appearing* while we were walking down the mountain.
6 The post *came* / *was coming* while we were having breakfast.

3 ●● Complete the sentences with the Past Simple or Past Continuous form of the verbs in brackets.
1 We *saw* (see) something strange in the sky while we *were looking* (look) at the stars.
2 The sun _____ (shine) when we _____ (arrive) at the beach.
3 While I _____ (wait) for the bus, I _____ (message) a few friends.
4 Jenna _____ (cry) when I finally _____ (find) her.
5 We first _____ (hear) about the storm while we _____ (have) dinner.
6 When I _____ (arrive) at Paula's house, she _____ (sit) outside in her garden.

4 ●●● Complete the dialogue with the Past Simple or Past Continuous form of the verbs below.

| do | eat | fall | have (x2) | hear | not rain |
| not stop | run | shine | start | tell | |

A: ¹*Did* you *have* a good time on your school trip last week?
B: Yes, we ² _____ a great time in the morning while the sun ³ _____. But it ⁴ _____ to rain while we ⁵ _____ our lunch, and it ⁶ _____ for the rest of the day!
A: Oh dear! What ⁷ _____ you _____ after lunch?
B: At first it ⁸ _____ very much, so our teacher ⁹ _____ us to keep looking for rocks near the river.
A: What happened next?
B: We ¹⁰ _____ thunder. I ¹¹ _____ to the bus when I ¹² _____ and dropped my camera. Now it doesn't work anymore.
A: Oh no!

I can use the Past Continuous and the Past Simple to talk about past events.

On the Portal
Extra Practice Activities: Lesson 2.4

2.5 Listening and Vocabulary
In the wild

1 Look at pictures A–H and write the words.

A

B

cave

C

D

E

F

G

H

2 Complete the sentences with the words below. There is one extra word.

bat ~~cave~~ path sky stars wildlife

1 It was very dark at the back of the _cave_.
2 At night you can see the _____ shining.
3 There is a lot of interesting _____ in the forest.
4 We followed the _____ until we came to a river.
5 There were only a few clouds in the _____.

I can understand a conversation about outdoor activities.

3 **WORD FRIENDS** Match the sentence halves.

1 [d] It was raining, so we made
2 [ ] It was cold, so we made
3 [ ] We listened
4 [ ] It's too cold to sleep
5 [ ] Last year scientists discovered
6 [ ] We looked
7 [ ] We watched

a to the wildlife all night.
b some unusual plants here.
c a fire to keep warm.
d ~~a shelter to keep us dry.~~
e the stars when we told stories.
f for wild animals, but didn't find any.
g outside.

4 🔊 2.1 Listen to the first part of a dialogue. What kind of summer camp did Alex go on?

a [ ] extreme fitness
b [ ] survival skills
c [ ] discovering wildlife

5 🔊 2.2 Listen to the second part of the dialogue. What happened on each day of the camp? Match days 1–5 with activities a–h. There are three extra activities.

DAYS		ACTIVITIES
1	day one	a making a fire
2	day two	b watching stars
3	day three	c discovering plants
4	day four	d watching a sunset
5	day five	e making a shelter
		f looking for wild animals
		g discovering a cave
		h finding water

On the Portal
Extra Practice Activities: Lesson 2.5

2.6 Speaking
Criticising and explaining

1 🔊 2.3 Listen and repeat the phrases.

> **SPEAKING Criticising and explaining**
>
> **Criticising**
> What's going on?
> Why did you do that?
>
> **Explaining and apologising**
> I can explain.   I'm so sorry.   I thought it was wrong.
> I didn't mean to break it.   I didn't realise it was yours.
>
> **Accepting explanations and apologies**
> I see.   That's all right.   Never mind.

2 Choose the correct option.
1. Why did you mean / *do* that? It wasn't fair.
2. I can *explain* / *realise*. It was Bob's fault.
3. Never *see* / *mind*. We can buy a new one.
4. That's *sorry* / *all right*. I know you didn't mean to upset me.
5. I didn't *realise* / *explain* it was yours. Sorry.
6. I *see* / *mind*. Just don't do it again.

3 Order the words to make sentences.
1. did / take / why / you / my / laptop / ?
   Why did you take my laptop?
2. thought / I / it / mine / was
   _____
3. on / what's / going / ?
   _____
4. hurt / didn't / you / mean / I / to
   _____

4 Complete the dialogues with the words below

> can   did   didn't   never   ~~on~~   see   so
> that's   thought   to

1. A: What's going *on*? Why are you in my room?
   B: I _____ explain. I heard a strange noise.
       I _____ it was a mouse.
   A: I _____ .
2. A: Why _____ you wake me up? It's the middle of the night.
   B: I didn't mean _____ . I _____ realise you were sleeping.
   A: _____ mind. Now go to bed!
3. A: I'm _____ sorry. I was using your phone and I dropped it. The screen smashed.
   B: _____ all right.

5 Choose the correct response.
1. You lost my phone! Why did you take it without asking?
   a I thought it was your phone.
   (b) I didn't mean to lose it.
   c Never mind.
2. Hey! Look at this big spider!
   a I didn't mean to scare you.
   b Oh, I'm sorry. I didn't realise.
   c Why did you do that? I hate spiders!
3. I'm so sorry. The dog ate your sandwich.
   a I see. That's all right.
   b What's going on?
   c Oh, I didn't mean to.
4. What's going on? Why are you riding my bike?
   a Why did you do that?
   b I can explain. I thought it was OK to use it.
   c I see. It's sunny today.

6 🔊 2.4 Complete the dialogues with one word in each gap. Listen and check.
1. Ella: Jack, where's my concert ticket from last night?
   Jack: I put it in the bin.
   Ella: *Why* did you do that?
   Jack: I _____ you didn't want it.
   Ella: Of course I want it – I want to keep it as a souvenir!
2. Tom: Look at this mess! What's going _____ ?
   Lisa: Err, I can _____ . I was trying to do some cooking and things went a bit wrong …
   Tom: Mum's coming home soon.
   Lisa: I didn't _____ to make a mess.
   Tom: I _____ . I can help you clear it up.
3. Kim: Why is my jumper all wet?
   Dora: I washed it for you.
   Kim: Why? It wasn't dirty.
   Dora: I'm so _____ . I wore it today and I dropped hot chocolate all over it.
   Kim: OK. That's all _____ . But next time ask me!

I can criticise and explain when things go wrong.

On the Portal
Extra Practice Activities: Lesson 2.6

2.7 Writing
An article describing your local area and climate

1 Read the article and answer the questions.
1. What is the temperature in Pokhara in January?
2. When is the rainy season in Pokhara?
3. What are two activities you can do in Pokhara?

Is Pokhara a good place to visit?

Pokhara, ¹*where* I live, is on the shores of Lake Phewa in Nepal. I think the climate here is ² _____ right. ³ _____ example, between November and February there is a lot of sunshine and it's usually between 20–25 degrees Celsius. However, there is a rainy season when a lot of rain falls. So don't come here between May and October if you don't like rain.

In Pokhara there are lots of ⁴ _____ you can do. Everywhere you look there are adventure sports to try. ⁵ _____ example is bungee jumping, and many tourists come here to go paragliding as well. Last month my friend came to visit and she wanted to do something less extreme. We took a boat on the lake and had a great time. In Pokhara you can also ⁶ _____ great food everywhere, such ⁷ _____ curry.

Everybody knows the Himalayan mountains are in Nepal. You can go on some amazing treks, ⁸ _____ the one I went on last year with my friends. We were walking for three days and the weather was fantastic. The sun was warm and the views were amazing. To sum up, Pokhara is a great place to visit. There isn't anywhere better!

2 Complete the article with the words below.

activities   as   find   for   just   like   one   ~~where~~

3 Choose the correct option.
1. I want to go *somewhere* / something exciting next year.
2. He wants to invite everything / everybody to his party.
3. Is there everything / anything to do here in winter?
4. The streets were really busy – there were people everywhere / anywhere.
5. Can we stop for a moment, there's anything / something in my shoe.
6. When I was on holiday, I didn't have anybody / everybody to talk to.

4 Complete Liam's notes with the words below.

city   kayaking   ~~mild~~   restaurant   see   snow

Area, weather, climate in Alaska
- long, freezing cold winters and ¹*mild* summers.
- very heavy ² _____
- Liam's hometown is the capital ³ _____, called Juneau. You get there by plane or boat.

Typical activities and places
- ⁴ _____ dolphins and whales
- go ⁵ _____ or camping
- eat in a traditional ⁶ _____

WRITING TIME

5 Imagine you are Liam. Write an article about your local area and climate using the notes in Exercise 4.

1 Find ideas
Make notes about:
- the weather, climate and things to do.
- a trip you went on. Think about the situation and what you did.

2 Plan and write
- Organise your ideas into paragraphs. Use the text about Pokhara to help you.
- Write a draft article.

3 Check
- Check language: did you use indefinite pronouns correctly?
- Check grammar: did you use the Past Simple and Past Continuous to illustrate your points?
- Write the final version of your article.

I can write an article about my local area and climate.

My Language File

WORDLIST 🔊 2.5

Word building (weather)
- cloud (n) _____
- cloudy (adj) _____
- fog (n) _____
- foggy (adj) _____
- ice (n) _____
- icy (adj) _____
- rain (n) _____
- rainy (adj) _____
- snow (n) _____
- snowy (adj) _____
- storm (n) _____
- stormy (adj) _____
- sun (n) _____
- sunny (adj) _____
- wind (n) _____
- windy (adj) _____

Weather
- breeze (n) _____
- drought (n) _____
- flood (n) _____
- gale (n) _____
- hurricane (n) _____
- lightning (n) _____
- shower (n) _____
- sunshine (n) _____
- thunder (n) _____

Word friends (weather and climate)
- boiling hot _____
- degrees Celsius _____
- freezing cold _____
- heavy rain _____
- heavy snow _____
- high/low temperature _____
- hot/mild/cold climate _____
- minus five degrees _____
- strong wind _____
- the temperature is rising/falling _____
- the weather is bad/cool/dry/fine/good/warm/wet _____

Adverbs of degree
- absolutely (boiling) (adv) _____
- completely (different) (adv) _____
- quite (worried) (adv) _____
- really (strange) (adv) _____
- totally (awesome) (adv) _____
- very (boring) (adv) _____

Word friends (camping)
- discover unusual plants _____
- listen to the wildlife _____
- look for wild animals _____
- make a fire _____
- make a shelter _____
- sleep outside _____
- watch the stars _____

In the wild
- bat (n) _____
- bear (n) _____
- cave (n) _____
- leaf (n) _____
- path (n) _____
- sky (n) _____
- spider (n) _____
- star (n) _____
- sunset (n) _____
- waterfall (n) _____
- wildlife (n) _____

Extra words
- adventure (n) _____
- Antarctic (n) _____
- Arctic (n) _____
- bright (adj) _____
- camping trip (n) _____
- conditions (n) _____
- degree (n) _____
- desert (n) _____
- find your way _____
- foreign (adj) _____
- freezing (adj) _____
- grow (v) _____
- huge (adj) _____
- lake (n) _____
- land (n) _____
- lighthouse (n) _____
- local (adj) _____
- melt (v) _____
- Milky Way (n) _____
- mountain (n) _____
- ocean (n) _____
- perfect (adj) _____
- planet (n) _____
- record-breaking (adj) _____
- root (n) _____
- sand dune (n) _____
- scared (adj) _____
- scorpion (n) _____
- sea level (n) _____
- sink (v) _____
- sleep in the open air _____
- soil (n) _____
- special (adj) _____
- treetop (n) _____
- volcano (n) _____
- wash away (v) _____
- weather forecast (n) _____

Sounds good!
- Can you give me a hand? _____
- No problem. _____
- Got it. _____

MY LANGUAGE NOTES

My favourite words/expressions from this unit

_____
_____
_____
_____
_____
_____
_____
_____

Self-check

Vocabulary

1 Complete the words in the sentences.
1 Look, it's a lovely s_____ day!
2 There was a g_____ at the weekend and some trees blew down.
3 We couldn't see very well because it was f_____.
4 It's quite m_____ today, so you don't need a coat.
5 Can I open the window? It's b_____ hot in here!
6 The temperature is twenty-seven d_____ today.
7 It rained for five days and there was a f_____ in our town.
8 Did you see the l_____ in the sky last night? It was amazing!

2 Complete the sentences with the words below.

| absolutely   awesome   boring   different |
| strange   worried |

1 This book was really _____. I didn't understand the ending at all.
2 You won the game! That's totally _____!
3 We were quite _____ when we saw the weather forecast.
4 It was _____ freezing at night in the desert.
5 I'm planning to go somewhere completely _____ this year.
6 I never play games on my smartphone. I think it's really _____.

3 Choose the correct option.
1 The *stars / leaves* fall off the trees in winter.
2 We found a small *path / sky* going through the forest.
3 We tried to *do / make* a shelter, but it was too difficult.
4 Scientists *looked / discovered* some unusual plants in the jungle.
5 We were looking *to / for* wild animals, but we didn't see any.
6 It was very dark in the *cave / sunset*.

Grammar

4 Complete the sentences with the Past Simple form of the verbs below.

| have   not see   not want   stay   take |

1 I _____ at the activity camp for three weeks.
2 We spent three weeks in Iceland, but we _____ the Northern Lights.
3 His first concert _____ place in London last week.
4 She _____ to touch the spider.
5 _____ you _____ a good time?

5 Choose the correct option.
1 I *saw / was seeing* a really big spider while I *walked / was walking* through the forest.
2 A lot of people *skied / were skiing* when the heavy snow *started / was starting* to fall.
3 We *watched / were watching* some amazing sunsets while we *stayed / were staying* in Scotland.
4 My brother *sat / was sitting* in the kitchen when I *got / was getting* home.
5 We *watched / were watching* TV *when / while* the hurricane started.

Speaking

6 Complete the dialogues with the phrases below.

| I didn't mean to   I didn't realise   I see   I thought |
| Why did you do that |

1 A: Where's my bike?
   B: I said that Jo could use it today.
   A: _____? I need it today.
   B: Sorry, _____ you needed it. _____ you were staying at home today.
2 A: Oh look – you burned the pizzas!
   B: Sorry, _____ burn them. The oven was too hot.
   A: _____.

YOUR SCORE

Vocabulary: __/20   Speaking: __/5
Grammar: __/15   Total: __/40

Tasty treats

VOCABULARY
Food | Cooking | Flavours | Word building: food | Collocations about food | Describing food

GRAMMAR
Present Perfect with *ever, never, just, already* and *yet* | Present Perfect with *for* and *since* | Present Perfect and Past Simple

3.1 Vocabulary
Food and drink

1 ● Complete the crossword with food words.

1 p
2 p e p p h
 p e
 v p
3 m 5 o e s
 r
6
 7
 s
8 p r
 m
 s

2 ● Choose the correct answer.
1 Which one is NOT a fruit?
  a garlic b pear c pineapple
2 Which one is a vegetable?
  a tuna b green pepper c oil
3 Which one is meat?
  a onion b nuts c sausage
4 Which one is fish?
  a mushroom b tuna c olives
5 Which one is NOT a vegetable?
  a onion b sweet potato c seeds
6 Which one is a fruit?
  a peach b pepper c chillies
7 Which one is used for frying?
  a nuts b oil c vinegar
8 Which one is NOT sweet?
  a pear b pineapple c nuts
9 Which one is a snack?
  a vinegar b nuts c garlic

3 ●● Choose the correct option.
1 I always put **pepper** / mushrooms on my chips.
2 I love fruit, especially *garlic / peach*.
3 My sister is vegetarian, so she doesn't eat *sausages / green peppers*.
4 First you fry the *onion / olives*, then you add the mushrooms.
5 I sometimes eat *vinegar / pineapple* in the morning.
6 You can add *chillies / seeds* to food to give it a hot taste.

4 ● Choose the correct option.
1 **boiled** / *flavour* potatoes
2 *frozen / roasted* yoghurt
3 difficult *raw / recipe*
4 *roasted / sauce* chicken
5 *fresh / fried* fruit
6 *frozen / fried* eggs
7 garlic *raw / sauce*
8 expensive *ingredients / recipes*
9 strong *flavour / frozen*

5 ●● Complete the sentences with the words below. There are two extra words.

| boiled | cooked | ~~frozen~~ | ingredients | raw |
| recipe | sauce | strong | | |

1 *Frozen* yoghurt is my favourite snack.
2 My sister likes _____ carrots, but I prefer them boiled.
3 I like to eat one hot _____ meal every day.
4 I'm not good at cooking. I always follow an easy _____.
5 My grandparents grow vegetables in their garden, so they always have fresh _____.
6 That _____ is too hot. I can't eat it.

Unit 3 26

6 ● Look at photos 1–8 and complete the words.

1 c<u>h o c o l a t e</u>   2 c_____

3 c_____   4 m_____

5 m_____   6 m_____

7 s_____   8 v_____

7 ●● Order the letters and write the words in the sentences.

> What's your favourite ice cream flavour?

1. I like fruit flavours like m<u>elon</u> (EMOLN) and s_____ (WABESRTRRY).

2. My favourite ice cream flavours are c_____ (LACOHOTEC) and v_____ (LAIVLNA). Mmm!

3. I love m_____ (MTNI) because it's a lovely cool flavour.

4. C_____ (NCCOOTU) is definitely my favourite! I like c_____ (FOECEF) as a drink, but I hate it as an ice cream flavour.

I can talk about food and drink.

8 ●●● Complete the texts with the words below.

| chocolate   flavours   fresh   ~~fried~~   mango |
| nuts   tuna |

At the weekend I usually eat a ¹*fried* egg with toast for breakfast, and drink a glass of ²_____ fruit juice. ³_____ is my favourite. For lunch, I often have a salad with ⁴_____ or maybe a sandwich. I don't eat many snacks like crisps because they aren't good for you. If I'm hungry, I often have a few ⁵_____ – my favourites are macadamia. And of course I also love ⁶_____, but I don't eat it every day.

| flavour   ingredients   pineapple   recipes |
| sausages   sweet potato |

I try to eat healthy food, so I don't eat meat such as ⁷_____. I eat a lot of vegetables, especially ⁸_____ – it's my favourite. I try to eat a lot of fruit because it's good for you – I really like ⁹_____. I enjoy cooking, so I often search for new ¹⁰_____ online. Sometimes it's hard to find all the ¹¹_____ in my local supermarket. My friends enjoy eating the food I cook. I use a lot of garlic and they love the ¹²_____!

9 ●●● Choose the correct option.
1. A: Mmm, I love this *raw* / (*fresh*) fruit cake!
   B: Thanks! I used my grandmother's *recipe* / *ingredients*.
   A: I can taste the *sweet potato* / *strawberries*. What's the other *flavour* / *sauce*?
   B: I added a little bit of *vanilla* / *vinegar* to make it sweet.
   A: It's delicious!

2. A: I don't usually like fish, but this *tuna* / *meat* is great. It tastes quite hot.
   B: That's because I added some *onion* / *chillies*. I also used some *roasted* / *boiled* garlic. It's easy to cook in the oven.

On the Portal
Extra Practice Activities: Lesson 3.1

3.2 Grammar
Present Perfect with *ever, never, just, already* and *yet*

> **GRAMMAR** — Present Perfect with *ever, never, just, already* and *yet*
>
> **Have** you **ever tried** beans on toast?
> **I've never heard** of anyone eating beans for breakfast.
> Bea**'s just got** up.
> **I've already eaten**.
> She **hasn't woken** up **yet**.
> **Have** you **finished yet**? Yes, I **have**./No, I **haven't**.

1 ● Complete the sentences with the Present Perfect form of the verbs in brackets.
1 I've *invited* (invite) all my friends to the party.
2 _____ (you/try) the brown sauce?
3 We _____ (not have) lunch yet.
4 Sasha _____ (eat) chocolate with chillies!
5 _____ (your dad/order) the pizzas yet?

2 ● Rewrite the sentences putting the words in brackets in the correct place.
1 Have you tried making bread? (ever)
   Have you ever tried making bread?
2 I've cooked a sweet potato. (never)
   _____
3 Molly has left. (just)
   _____
4 We haven't finished eating. (yet)
   _____
5 I've had lunch. (already)
   _____
6 Have you eaten food from another country? (ever)
   _____

3 ● Make sentences in the Present Perfect. Use the words in brackets.
1 you / make / dinner / for / your friends / ? (ever)
   Have you ever made dinner for your friends?
2 the film / start (already)
   _____
3 your email / not arrive (yet)
   _____
4 you / make / Sara's birthday cake / ? (yet)
   _____
5 Mike / cook / a meal (never)
   _____
6 we / order / our food (just)
   _____

4 ●● Choose the correct option.
1 Have you *ever* / yet eaten coconut ice cream?
2 I've *never / already* seen that film, so I don't want to see it again.
3 Have you cooked the onion *yet / ever*?
4 Jo isn't here – she's *just / yet* left.
5 I've *ever / never* tried fresh tuna.
6 I haven't finished my homework *yet / already*.

5 ●●● Complete the dialogues. Use the Present Perfect.
1 A: *Have you finished your homework yet?* (you/finish/your homework/yet)?
   B: No, I _____. But Tara _____ (do/already) all the Maths exercises, so she can help me!
2 A: _____ (you/try/ever) a fruit smoothie?
   B: Yes, I _____. I've got a smoothie maker, and I _____ (make/just) a pineapple and peach smoothie – delicious!

6 ●●● Complete the email with one word in each gap.

Hi Maya,

I hope you can still come round to my house later for the film night. I ¹*'ve* made some tuna and olive pizzas – yes, I made them myself! Have you ² _____ tried making your own pizza? I haven't tasted them ³ _____ because I've ⁴ _____ taken them out of the oven, so they're still really hot. I hope they taste good! I've also bought some mango ice cream. I've ⁵ _____ tried this flavour before, but it looks tasty. Jake ⁶ _____ already told me he can come, which is great, but I ⁷ _____ heard from Cara ⁸ _____. I hope she can come.

See you later!
Niki

I can use the Present Perfect to talk about experiences.

On the Portal
Extra Practice Activities: Lesson 3.2

3.3 Reading and Vocabulary
Super healthy foods

1 Choose the correct option.
1 My favourite fruit is a *juice* / *juicy* mango.
2 Raw carrots are *crunch* / *crunchy*.
3 Can you pass me the *salt* / *salty*?
4 I never put *butter* / *buttery* on my toast.
5 I love eating *crisps* / *crispy* for a snack.
6 Wow, this soup is so *cream* / *creamy*.
7 Did you add *spice* / *spicy* to the curry?
8 Orange is a very *health* / *healthy* fruit.
9 I don't eat meat. It's too *fat* / *fatty* for me.
10 The meal was really *taste* / *tasty*.

2 **WORD FRIENDS** Complete the sentences with prepositions below.

~~for~~   from   of   to   with

1 I try to eat foods that are healthy *for* me.
2 Scientists say some foods can protect people _____ illness.
3 Superfoods are often full _____ vitamins.
4 Chocolate goes well _____ fresh fruit.
5 I don't add sugar _____ smoothies.

3 Read the article quickly and choose the correct answer.
The article looks at four foods which
a are cheap and healthy.
b are healthy and good for the environment.
c are healthy but expensive.

4 Read the article again and complete the sentences with 1–3 words from the article.
1 The main ingredients in vegetable meat are *plants and vegetables*.
2 Vegetable meat uses less _____ than meat from animals.
3 Laboratory meat is good with _____.
4 It's _____ to make laboratory meat at the moment.
5 Algae don't taste _____.
6 Tiger nuts won't hurt people with _____.
7 You might see Tiger nuts _____.

I can understand an article about superfoods.

SUPERFOODS
OF THE FUTURE

I love eating superfoods to stay healthy, but are they good for the planet? Try these four foods which are healthy, tasty and eco-friendly.

Juicy burgers, spicy sausages or roast chicken. Meat lovers can now find vegetarian versions of their favourite foods. Vegetable meat looks, smells and tastes like meat, but they make it from plants and vegetables. It's good for your health and it tastes delicious. What's more, it doesn't take as much energy and water to produce as real meat, so it's great for the environment too!

It's not science fiction. It is real! Scientist have made real meat in a laboratory which is 100 percent vegetarian. You don't need to cut down trees to build big farms, so it's good for the environment. This meat isn't fatty and it goes well with chips and potatoes. Unfortunately, at the moment it's very expensive to produce, so I haven't tried it yet. But I've heard it's very tasty.

Green, brown or red. We usually see these underwater plants at the beach. Algae contain Omega-3 fatty acids and are full of vitamins. You can easily add them to tasty smoothies, too. They don't taste like fish at all and they have a nice flavour. The best thing about algae is that they don't hurt the environment – they don't need anything special to grow and they even help to keep water clean.

Have you ever eaten Tiger nuts? These snacks look and taste like nuts, but they are actually a type of vegetable similar to a sweet potato. That means people with nut allergies can eat them. You can eat them raw, roasted or boiled and they are good for your health. They even help to protect people from certain diseases. They are very easy to grow. You could even find them in your garden!

3.4 Grammar

Present Perfect with *for* and *since* | Present Perfect and Past Simple

GRAMMAR — Present Perfect with *for* and *since* | Present Perfect and Past Simple

Present Perfect with *for* and *since*
I've lived in Rio **for** many years. (a period of time)
They've had this bar **since** 1970. (a point in time)

Present Perfect and Past Simple
We've **been to** São Paulo.
We **went** to São Paulo in 2012.
Have you ever **drunk** a mango smoothie?
Did you **like** it?

1 ● Write the words below in the correct column.

1998	a couple of hours	a long time	~~five minutes~~
five o'clock	four weeks	I was a child	last weekend
ten minutes	two years	Wednesday	yesterday

for – a period of time	*since* – a point in time
five minutes	

2 ●● Complete the sentences with *for* or *since*.
1 We've been here *for* nearly an hour, and the train hasn't arrived yet!
2 There has been a juice bar here _____ 2002.
3 We haven't had any homework _____ Monday.
4 Mr Thomas has worked at this school _____ over twenty years.
5 Tom has been at college _____ a few months now and he loves it.
6 I've had this phone _____ last summer.

3 ●● Choose the correct option.
1 I (went) / have been to New York two years ago.
2 This restaurant *opened* / *has opened* in 2015.
3 We *lived* / *have lived* in this house for two months now, so it's beginning to feel like home.
4 I *knew* / *have known* Paul since I was five years old – he's my best friend.
5 *Did you see* / *Have you seen* Emily yesterday?
6 *Did you ever go* / *Have you ever been* to Paris?

4 ●● Complete the dialogues with the Present Perfect or Past Simple form of the verbs in brackets.
1 A: *Have you seen* (you/see) the new James Bond film yet?
   B: Yes, I _____ (see) it last night.
2 A: I _____ (never/try) pear juice. Is it nice?
   B: Yes. I _____ (try) some last summer. It was lovely!
3 A: _____ (you/meet) the new boy in our class yet?
   B: Yes, I _____ (meet) him yesterday. He's really nice.
4 A: Jack _____ (not do) his Maths homework. What about you?
   B: I _____ (do) it at the weekend. It was quite difficult!

5 ●●● Complete the texts with the Present Perfect or Past Simple form of the verbs in brackets.

I ¹*went* (go) to the Chinese restaurant in Dalton Street last night. ² _____ (you/eat) there? The food's really nice. I ³ _____ (have) some tuna, which ⁴ _____ (be) very tasty!

I ⁵ _____ (try) that restaurant. I ⁶ _____ (not like) it at all. But that ⁷ _____ (be) about six months ago.

I think the food ⁸ _____ (improve) since last year. Two of my friends ⁹ _____ (eat) there last Saturday and they ¹⁰ _____ (never have) a better meal!

6 ●●● Complete the dialogues with one word in each gap.
1 A: ¹*Have* you ever drunk coconut milk?
   B: Yes, I ² _____. I tried it about two years ago, but I ³ _____ like it. I haven't tried it again ⁴ _____ then.
2 A: Have you ⁵ _____ to the new Pizza Palace restaurant yet?
   B: No, I ⁶ _____. Where is it?
   A: It's on Clarence Street. It's been open ⁷ _____ about six weeks now.

Unit 3 — I can use the Present Perfect and the Past Simple to talk about experiences.

On the Portal
Extra Practice Activities: Lesson 3.4

3.5 Listening and Vocabulary
A dream cake

1 Complete the words for describing food.
1 sw _e_ _e_ t
2 h _ _ d
3 b _ tt _ r
4 s _ _ r
5 r _ _ h
6 d _ y
7 d _ l _ c _ _ _ s
8 h _ t

2 Choose the correct option.
1 My grandpa can't eat raw carrots because they are too *hard* / *sour* for him.
2 Mint ice cream is my favourite – it's *hot* / *delicious*!
3 It's a lovely sauce, but it's quite *rich* / *hard*, so I can't eat very much.
4 Don't add too much sugar – I don't like food that's too *bitter* / *sweet*.
5 This bread is horrible. It's so *fresh* / *dry*!
6 Lemon juice is too *hot* / *sour* to drink.

3 🔊 3.1 Listen to Lily talking about the cake she has made. Mark the sentences T (true) or F (false).
1 ☐ Lily has made a cake for her friends.
2 ☐ She has made cakes since she was ten.
3 ☐ Her cake is in the shape of a boat.
4 ☐ It's a chocolate cake.
5 ☐ The filling is red.
6 ☐ You can read a message on the cake.

4 🔊 3.2 Listen to information about the competition Lily entered. Complete the advert.

School cake competition
Are you a champion baker? Our school cake competition takes place soon. Why not make a cake and bring it along? You never know – you might win!
Date of competition: ¹ _29_ June
Bring cakes to the school cookery room before ² _____ o'clock
Last year's winning novelty cake: a cake in the shape of a(n) ³ _____
Entry cost: ⁴ £_____ per cake
Prize: a(n) ⁵ _____ and £25
Entry forms available from Mrs Cussons or the ⁶ _____

5 🔊 3.2 Choose the correct option. Listen again and check.
1 If you're *taking* / *doing* part, you need to bring your cake to the school cookery room.
2 Mrs Addison will *give* / *announce* the winner.
3 If you'd like to *enter* / *make* the competition, you need an entry form.
4 You need to *write* / *fill* in your entry form by next week.
5 Someone's going to *win* / *earn* that prize!

I can understand people describing food.

3.6 Speaking
Ordering food

1 🔊 **3.3 Listen and repeat the phrases.**

SPEAKING | **Ordering food**

Customer
I'll have/I'd like a slice of pumpkin pie.
Excuse me, can/could we have/share a starter?
Excuse me, can/could I share a starter with you?
Just water for me, please.
Have you got any vegetable dishes?
Not for me, thanks.

Waiter
Take a seat and I'll get you the menu.
What would you like to drink?
Are you ready to order?
Would you like anything else/to eat?
Can I get you something?
For the/your starter/main course/dessert?
Here you are.

2 Match the sentence halves.
1 [c] Take a seat and   a you something?
2 [ ] What would you   b you are.
3 [ ] Would you like anything c I'll get you the menu.
4 [ ] Here   d starter?
5 [ ] Are you ready   e to order?
6 [ ] Can I get   f like to drink?
7 [ ] For your   g to eat?

3 Complete the sentences with the words below.

| any | ~~excuse~~ | have | please | thanks |

1 _Excuse_ me, can I have some water?
2 Not for me, _____ .
3 Just a smoothie for me, _____ .
4 I'll _____ a coffee, please.
5 Have you got _____ chocolate cake, please?

4 Find and correct the mistakes in the sentences.
1 Get a seat and I'll get you the menu.
   Take a seat and I'll get you the menu.
2 What would you to drink?
   _____
3 Can I have you something?
   _____
4 Not me, thanks.
   _____
5 Excuse, can I have some water?
   _____

5 Choose the correct response.
1 Would you like anything to eat?
   a Here you are.
   (b) Not for me, thanks.
   c Can I get you something?
2 Excuse me, can I have a strawberry smoothie, please?
   a Thanks.
   b Are you ready to order?
   c Here you are.
3 Can I get you something?
   a Excuse me.
   b Just a sandwich for me, please.
   c Take a seat.
4 Have you got any cake?
   a Yes, I'll get you the menu.
   b Are you ready to order?
   c Can I get you something?

6 🔊 **3.4 Complete the dialogues with one word in each gap. Listen and check.**

1 Waiter: Hello. Are you _ready_ to order?
  Max: Yes. Can I _____ a banana smoothie, please?
  Waiter: Of course. And would you like _____ to eat?
  Max: Have you got _____ soup?
  Waiter: No, not today. Sorry.
  Max: OK, no problem. _____ the smoothie for me, please.

2 Rob: Hi! I'm sorry I'm late.
  Leah: That's OK. I've just ordered an ice cream, but the waiter hasn't brought it yet. What would you _____ to eat?
  Rob: Oh, ice cream sounds nice. Where's the waiter? Er, _____ me, can I _____ a vanilla ice cream, please?
  Waiter: Yes, of course. _____ you like anything to drink?
  Rob: _____ for me, thanks. Just the ice cream.

Unit 3 | 32 | I can order food in a café or restaurant.

On the Portal
Extra Practice Activities: Lesson 3.6

3.7 Writing
An email to a friend

1 Order the letters and write the verbs in the sentences.
1. You need a knife to c_hop_ (HCPO) the onions and carrots.
2. F_____ (RYF) the garlic in a bit of oil.
3. S_____ (LIESC) the tomato and put it on top of the pizza.
4. Carefully p_____ (RUOP) the smoothie into the glass.
5. Slowly a_____ (DDA) the milk.

2 Complete the email with the phrases below.

| are things | can't wait | decided to have | great to hear | I was wondering | just finished | let me know |

Hi Tanya,

How ¹_are things_? It was ²_____ from you last week. I ³_____ to hear more about your new school.
We've ⁴_____ our exams here – the Maths exam was really difficult! We've ⁵_____ a class lunch to celebrate the end of the year. It's next Thursday. The plan is for everyone to make a tasty dish and then we can all share the food. I'm making a pizza. I buy the pizza base, of course. First, I fry some onions and garlic. Next, I chop some tomatoes and mix them with the onions. After that I put that mixture onto the pizza base. Then I boil one or two eggs, I slice them and put them on the pizza. Finally, I slice some delicious cheese to put on top.

Anyway, ⁶_____ if you'd like to come. We'd all be really pleased to see you again.

⁷_____ if you can make it.

Rob

3 Choose the correct option in the recipe below.

¹(First)/ Then I mix egg and cinnamon in a bowl. ²Finally / Next, I pour in some milk and mix again. ³After that / First, I put the bread in the mixture. ⁴Finally / Then I fry the bread on both sides. ⁵Next / Finally, I sit down and eat my breakfast!

4 Order the words to make phrases for an email to a friend.
1. to ask / like to come / I'm writing / if you'd
   I'm writing to ask if you'd like to come.
2. soon / see / you
   _____
3. great / your holiday / it was / to hear about
   _____
4. in touch / thanks / for getting
   _____
5. for / now / bye
   _____

5 Complete the notes with the words below.

| at her new school | I'm making | invite her | next Friday | suggest what she | to email |

- remember ¹_to email_ Marta (our class last year)
- glad she's happy ²_____
- tell her about class lunch ³_____
- tell her what ⁴_____
- ⁵_____ to the lunch
- ⁶_____ should bring

WRITING TIME

6 Write an email to Marta using the notes in Exercise 5.

1 Find ideas
Make notes about:
- where and when you're having the party.
- what you're celebrating.
- what food you're planning to make.

2 Plan and write
- Organise your ideas into paragraphs. Use Rob's email to help you.
- Write a draft email.

3 Check
- Check language: did you use sequencers and imperatives for your recipe?
- Check grammar: did you use the Present Perfect correctly?
- Write the final version of your email.

I can write an email to a friend. 33 Unit 3

My Language File

WORDLIST 🔊 3.5

Food
chillies (n) _____
garlic (n) _____
green pepper (n) _____
mushroom (n) _____
nuts (n) _____
oil (n) _____
olives (n) _____
onion (n) _____
peach (n) _____
pear (n) _____
pepper (n) _____
pineapple (n) _____
sausage (n) _____
seeds (n) _____
sweet potato (n) _____
tuna (n) _____
vinegar (n) _____

Cooking
boiled (adj) _____
cooked (adj) _____
flavour (n) _____
fresh (adj) _____
fried (adj) _____
frozen (adj) _____
ingredients (n) _____
raw (adj) _____
recipe (n) _____
roasted (adj) _____
sauce (n) _____

Flavours
chocolate (adj) _____
coconut (adj) _____
coffee (adj) _____
mango (adj) _____
melon (adj) _____
mint (adj) _____
strawberry (adj) _____
vanilla (adj) _____

Word building (food)
butter – buttery _____
cream – creamy _____
crisp – crispy _____
crunch – crunchy _____
fat – fatty _____
health – healthy _____
juice – juicy _____
salt – salty _____
spice – spicy _____
taste – tasty _____

Word friends
(collocations about food)
add to (v) _____
full of (adj) _____
go well with _____
good/healthy for (adj) _____
protect from (v) _____

Describing food
bitter (adj) _____
delicious (adj) _____
dry (adj) _____
hard (adj) _____
hot (adj) _____
rich (adj) _____
sour (adj) _____
spicy (adj) _____
sweet (adj) _____

Extra words
bakery (n) _____
beef (n) _____
body (n) _____
bone (n) _____
carrot (n) _____
cereal (n) _____
chips (n) _____
chop (v) _____
cool (adj) _____
curry (n) _____
dairy (n) _____
dessert (n) _____
eyesight (n) _____
flour (n) _____
heart (n) _____
honey (n) _____
leaf/leaves (n) _____
meal (n) _____
meat (n) _____
medicine (n) _____
menu (n) _____
mix (v) _____
peanuts (n) _____
pickles (n) _____
pie (n) _____
plate (n) _____
pour (v) _____
salad (n) _____
salmon (n) _____
serious (adj) _____
skin (n) _____
slice (v, n) _____
smell (n) _____
snack (n) _____
strange (adj) _____
surprising (adj) _____
survey (n) _____
taste (v) _____
toast (n) _____
topping (n) _____
treats (n) _____
vegetarian (n) _____

Sounds good!
Sure thing. _____
Hold on! _____
You must be joking! _____

MY LANGUAGE NOTES

My favourite words/expressions from this unit

Self-check

Vocabulary

1 Choose the odd one out.
1 **Fruit:** garlic, peach, pear
2 **Vegetables:** green pepper, sweet potato, pineapple
3 **Meat and fish:** sausage, tuna, chillies
4 **Snacks:** seeds, vinegar, nuts
5 **Cooking:** ingredients, ice cream, recipe
6 **Flavours:** coconut, mint, sauce

2 Choose the correct option.
1 Our school lunches are always *health / healthy*.
2 *Crunch / Crunchy* vegetables are my favourite.
3 This yoghurt is so *cream / creamy*.
4 There is so much *juice / juicy* in this mango.
5 Fish is healthy *for / with* your brain.
6 Some foods can protect *to / from* illness.
7 I usually add extra pepper *to / for* recipes.
8 Garlic goes well *with / for* mushrooms.

3 Choose the correct answer.
1 Some people say coffee tastes ___.
   a bitter   b hot   c dry
2 The bread is ___, so we can't eat it anymore.
   a fresh   b hard   c delicious
3 Curry is often very ___.
   a bitter   b hard   c hot
4 I made a cake, but it was ___, so it didn't taste good.
   a fresh   b tasty   c dry
5 Lemons taste ___.
   a sour   b sweet   c rich
6 The pineapple was very ___.
   a rich   b sweet   c sour

Grammar

4 Complete the sentences with the Present Perfect form of the verbs in brackets.
1 Don't worry, we _____ (not order/yet). Here's a menu.
2 _____ (you/try/ever) chilli chocolate?
3 Come in – we _____ (finish/just) eating.
4 I _____ (see/never) Tim so angry before!
5 _____ (it/stop) raining yet?
6 _____ (you/cook/ever) a meal for 10 people?
7 He _____ (won/just) a competition!

5 Complete the sentences with the Present Perfect or Past Simple form of the verbs in brackets.
1 I _____ (visit) Paris a few times. It's a lovely city.
2 We _____ (not go) away on holiday last year.
3 Everyone _____ (enjoy) the meal last night.
4 A new café _____ (just/open) near our school.
5 I _____ (write) an email to Max three days ago, but he _____ (not reply) yet.
6 I _____ (never/have) a chocolate smoothie, but I _____ (try) a coconut smoothie last summer.

Speaking

6 Complete the dialogues with the words and phrases below. There is one extra phrase.

> excuse me   I'll have   not for me   something to drink   you are   your starter

1 A: Are you ready to order?
   B: _____ a salad please.
2 A: Can I get you _____?
   B: Could I have some fresh juice, please?
3 A: _____, can I have some water, please?
   B: Of course.
4 A: For _____?
   B: Could I have some olives, please?
5 A: Here _____.
   B: Thanks.

YOUR SCORE

Vocabulary: __/20   Speaking: __/5
Grammar: __/15   **Total:** __/40

Reading Time 1

Sharks

Freddy lives on a Pacific Island. There, the fishermen – and Freddy's father – can only make good money from shark finning*. Will sharks have to die so Freddy can go to college? Or can he and his friends bring money to the island and protect the sharks?

Kristin got up early. She liked running on the beach in the mornings. She put on her running shoes and went down to the ocean. When she got to the beach, she saw some women there, and a boat in the water. The boat came nearer and nearer. Kristin could see the fishermen on the boat. They had something in their hands.

'The men are throwing something to the women on the beach,' thought Kristin, 'but what?'

The women were busy. They didn't see her. Suddenly, Kristin stopped. She could see now. It was a shark fin!

She heard a noise behind her and turned around. It was Freddy.

'Go away, Kristin. I don't want you to see this,' he said quietly.

'But Freddy, why are they doing this? Don't they know that the sharks will die?' Kristin answered angrily.

'Kristin, change comes slowly. Things are changing here, but you have to understand the islanders. They don't have much money. What can they do? They can make money from those fins.'

The two new friends walked away from the beach. They didn't speak and they didn't look back at the beach. After some time, they came to a quiet place on the road and sat down under a tree.

Kristin turned to Freddy. 'Listen to me, Freddy. I have an idea. Maybe it's the answer to the problems here.'

'I'm listening,' said Freddy.

'A lot of people love to dive,' Kristin said, 'and want to learn about life in the ocean. Do you know about *Shark Week* on TV? For seven days, they show movies about sharks and talk about them. My friend Gemma watches hours and hours of TV that week! She makes friends with other people on the internet, and they plan shark vacations. They go to Palau and the Marshall Islands, to Hawaii and South Africa, to Mexico and Australia, and everywhere they see sharks.'

'This island – your island – is beautiful. Divers will love it. We can talk to Pam and her parents at the hotel, and to your parents and your friends on the island. Some people can open their homes to visitors and make some money. Other people can start restaurants. Fishermen can take the tourists out in their boats. There will be work for everybody!'

'Yes,' said Freddy slowly. 'So we won't have to go on shark finning trips. The tourists will bring money to the island.'

'That's right!' said Kristin.

Before you read

1 Match sentences 1–4 with pictures A–D.
1 Fishermen catch sharks and sell their fins.
2 The islanders love living on their island.
3 Lots of divers come here to explore the sea.
4 I love watching films and programmes about sharks on TV during Shark Week.

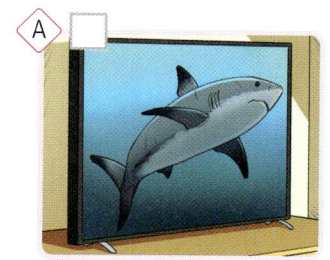

2 Look at the book cover and read the blurb. What do you think happens in the story?

While you read

3 🔊 RT1.1 Read and listen to the story. Choose the correct option.
1 Freddy *likes / doesn't like* shark finning (taking fins from sharks).
2 The islanders *don't make / make* money from shark finning.
3 Freddy *doesn't use / uses* money from shark finning to go to college.
4 Freddy and his friend *have an idea / don't have any ideas* how to make money in other ways.

4 Read the story again. Put sentences a–f in the correct order.
a ☐ Freddy and Kristin leave the beach.
b ☐ Kristin sees the islanders with a shark fin.
c ☐ Freddy agrees with Kristin's idea.
d ☐ Kristin goes for a run.
e ☐ Freddy explains to Kristin what's happening on the beach.
f ☐ Kristin tells Freddy about Shark Week.

5 Choose the correct answer.
1 The women on the beach ____
 a know that Kristin is there.
 b don't know that Kristin is there.
 c speak to Kristin.
2 Kristin felt ____ when she saw the shark fins.
 a frightened   b angry   c excited
3 During Shark Week, people can spend seven days ____
 a swimming with sharks.
 b travelling to different places.
 c watching movies about sharks.
4 People travel ____ to see sharks.
 a around the island   b from the island
 c all over the world
5 They think tourists will ____
 a be good for the island.
 b be bad for the island.
 c buy shark fins.

After you read

6 Complete the sentences with a word from box A and a word from box B in the correct form. Then check your answers in the story.

A
get go put talk take

B
about away on out up

1 Kristin _____ _____ early.
2 She _____ _____ her running shoes and went down to the beach.
3 '_____ _____, Kristin. I don't want you to see this.'
4 For seven days, they show movies about sharks and _____ _____ them.
5 Fishermen can _____ the tourists _____ in their boats.

7 **WRAP UP** Complete the information about the story.

Title: _____
Type: *love story / horror story / adventure story*
Main characters: _____
Important object: _____
My opinion: ☆☆☆☆☆

Entertain us!

VOCABULARY
Types of film | Word building: entertainment | Film and TV | Collocations: music | Compound nouns

GRAMMAR
Comparatives and superlatives, too/(not) enough, (not) as … as | Quantifiers

4.1 Vocabulary
Film and TV

1 ● Complete the words for types of films.
1. c o m e d y
2. d_ _ _ _ m_ n_ _ _ y
3. ac_ _ _ _ n
4. s_ _ e_ _ _ _ f_ c_ _ _ _ n
5. m_ s_ _ _ l
6. c_ _ t_ _ n
7. d_ _ _ a
8. t_ _ _ ll_ r
9. r_ m_ _ c_

2 ●● Read the descriptions and write the types of films.
1. It's a beautiful love story. *romance*
2. It's so funny! The actors really made me laugh! _____
3. It takes place in the future, on a different planet. _____
4. It's a really interesting film about lions. _____
5. It's a story about people's lives and all the things that happen to them. _____
6. The characters are drawings, not real people. _____
7. There are some amazing car chases. _____
8. A story with lots of singing and dancing. _____
9. It was so exciting – I didn't know what was going to happen! _____

3 ● Complete the table.

Noun	Person	Verb
¹*acting*	² _____	act
entertainment	entertainer	³ _____
performance	performer	⁴ _____
production	⁵ _____	produce
⁶ _____	reviewer	review

4 ●● Choose the correct option.
1. I think Jennifer Lawrence is a brilliant act / (actor).
2. This Masala film is great entertainer / entertainment for all the family.
3. I'd love to work as a film producer / production.
4. I'd be too scared to perform / performance in front of thousands of people.
5. The film didn't get good reviewers / reviews in the newspapers.

5 ● Match the sentence halves.
1. [d] The main character in the film
2. [ ] The show was an instant
3. [ ] When did the story first appear
4. [ ] A new science fiction
5. [ ] What's your favourite
6. [ ] The TV audience

a. hit – everyone loved it!
b. loved it.
c. TV show?
d. ~~is a fifteen-year-old boy.~~
e. series is starting tonight.
f. on our TV screens?

6 ●● Complete the sentences with the words below.

| channel | ~~episode~~ | hit | series | special effects | viewers |

1. The new *episode* of my favourite programme is on next week.
2. This programme is especially popular with young _____.
3. It's no surprise that the movie won several awards for its _____ – they are absolutely amazing.
4. Can we change the _____? I don't like this programme.
5. The producers were really happy that the show was such a big _____.
6. *The Mandalorian* was the first *Star Wars* television _____ with live actors.

Unit 4 38

7 ●● Choose the correct answer.
1. We went to see a(n) ___ at the cinema and the songs was amazing.
   a documentary   b episode
   c musical
2. I changed the ___ because there were too many commercials.
   a screen   b channel
   c actions
3. I'd like to work as a(n) ___. I love films and I'm good at planning.
   a entertainer   b viewer
   c producer
4. Let's go see the new ___. I need a good laugh!
   a comedy   b thriller
   c character
5. I've started a blog to ___ all the films I watch.
   a produce   b review
   c act
6. They wanted to make a show for a young ___.
   a director   b production
   c audience
7. I prefer good acting to lots of expensive ___.
   a performers   b special effects
   c hits
8. Before he was famous, he was in an awful ___ about zombies.
   a character   b channel   c TV show

8 ●●● Complete the text with one word in each gap.

What's on tonight?
Our ¹*reviewers* give their suggestions for the best shows on TV tonight.

| Hot and Cold | Channel 3 | 6:30 |

A ² ___ about how animals live in the hottest and coldest places in the world. Great ³ ___ for all the family.

| Maxwell Street | BTV | 7:30 |

Is Kerry in danger? Don't miss this week's ⁴ ___ of this exciting drama ⁵ ___. It isn't surprising that *Maxwell Street* is such a big ⁶ ___. There are no ⁷ ___ effects, but the story is great and the ⁸ ___, Damien Green, is brilliant as Jake, the lovable hero.

| Don't call me | The **Movie** Channel | 8:00 |

If ⁹ ___ is your favourite kind of film, make sure you watch this amazing love story. Carrie Taylor gives a great ¹⁰ ___ as Emma, the main ¹¹ ___ in the film. What's it about? Well, if you want to know the story, I suggest you go and see the film! It had very good ¹² ___ when it first came out in cinemas and it's great to see it now on our TV screens.

I can talk about films and television.

4.2 Grammar
Comparatives and superlatives, too/(not) enough, (not) as … as

GRAMMAR — Comparatives and superlatives, too/(not) enough, (not) as … as

Comparatives
The screens are bigger.   It's more exciting than 3-D.

Superlatives
It's the latest 4-D experience.
The most exciting scene was in the car.
It's the best feeling in the world.

too/(not) enough
I was too uncomfortable.   My car wasn't fast enough.

(not) as … as
The experience isn't as good as 3-D.

1 ● Complete the sentences with the comparative or superlative form of the adjectives in brackets.
1. I think the second film is *better* (good) than the first one.
2. The _____ (funny) part was when he fell in the swimming pool.
3. I think that having a good story is _____ (important) than having famous actors.
4. These are the _____ (uncomfortable) seats I've ever sat on!
5. Going to the cinema is _____ (exciting) than watching a film at home.
6. That's the _____ (bad) film I've ever seen – it was awful!

2 ● Choose the correct answer.
1. That film was ____!
   a) too scary   b) enough scary   c) as scary as
2. The story isn't ____.
   a) enough exciting   b) exciting enough   c) exciting as
3. These seats aren't ____ the others.
   a) as expensive as   b) expensive as   c) too expensive as
4. You're ____ to see that film.
   a) too young   b) enough young   c) as young
5. The actors weren't ____ for me to hear.
   a) too loud   b) enough loud   c) loud enough

3 ● Choose the correct option.
1. Action films are more exciting *that / than* romances.
2. It's *funnier / the funniest* film I've ever seen!
3. The second part of the film was worse *from / than* the first part.
4. The seats aren't *too / as* big as our chairs at home.
5. It wasn't *enough interesting / interesting enough* for me.

4 ●● Decide if the sentences in each pair have the same meaning (S) or a different meaning (D).
1. **D** a Jack isn't as old as his brother.
        b Jack and his brother are the same age.
2. ____ a The new cinema is bigger than the old one.
        b The old cinema isn't as big as the new one.
3. ____ a The tickets are too expensive for us.
        b The tickets are cheap enough for us.
4. ____ a This is the most exciting film ever!
        b No film is as exciting as this one!
5. ____ a These new seats are as uncomfortable as the old ones.
        b The old seats were more comfortable.

5 ●●● Complete the forum posts with the correct form of the adjectives in brackets. Add any other words as necessary.

Has anyone seen a 4-D film? I saw one last night and it was ¹*the best* (good) experience of my life! It was definitely much ² _____ (exciting) a normal film.

I saw a 4-D film last week, but it wasn't ³ _____ (good) I expected. The moving seats were ⁴ _____ (uncomfortable) for me to relax and enjoy the film.

I tried to see a 4-D film last week, but I was with my little sister and she wasn't ⁵ _____ (old) to watch the film. She wasn't as ⁶ _____ (disappointed) I was because I took her for a pizza instead!

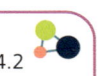

I can use the comparative and superlative of adjectives to describe things.

On the Portal
Extra Practice Activities: Lesson 4.2

4.3 Reading and Vocabulary
How do you listen to music?

1 Read the blog post. Which person talks about these things: Cara, Javier, Yuki or Karol?
1. scientific research _____
2. getting good reviews _____
3. starting university _____
4. going to a concert _____

2 Read the blog post again and choose the correct answer.
1. a an event   b a live   c an audience
2. a train   b record   c practise
3. a track   b music   c lyrics
4. a as   b than   c from
5. a write   b make   c play
6. a time   b live   c life

3 WORD FRIENDS Choose the correct option.
1. It isn't easy to *write* / *make* lyrics.
2. Sometimes I *sing* / *listen* along to songs.
3. The band *downloaded* / *livestreamed* the concert, so I watched it from home.
4. I downloaded my best friend's *lyrics* / *playlist*. I love her taste in music.
5. My favourite singer has just *recorded* / *downloaded* a new track. I love it.
6. Do you like *going* / *making* to live performances?
7. I never buy CDs, I only *stream* / *get* music.
8. Do you *lip-synch* / *record* to music videos?

Playing a musical instrument makes you happy

Most people like listening to music, but what about playing a musical instrument? I've asked some of my friends to share their experiences of learning to make music.

I decided to learn the piano after going to ¹_____ performance. I've been to lots of concerts, but this was the best. Playing the piano is not as difficult as it looks, but you have to ²_____ a lot. My favourite thing is playing for other people. I love seeing how happy music makes them. It also helps me to relax. I like playing before I do my homework. Everything is better when you feel relaxed.

I've always loved the violin, but my parents thought school was more important ⁴_____ music. I decided to do some research and show them how learning an instrument is good for the brain. Scientists say that it can make you smarter! Now I play in my school orchestra. Last year we livestreamed a concert, and thousands of viewers watched it.

I started playing the guitar when I was ten, but I didn't work very hard and I was the worst in my group. Then last year I moved schools and it was more difficult to make friends than I expected. When my school organised a music competition, I decided to take part. It was a good idea! Now I'm in a band and I've got some new friends. Last month we played a concert and we've even recorded a ³_____! We got great reviews online.

I play the drums and sometimes I ⁵_____ lyrics too. I'm quite shy and my hobby helps me to be more confident. I'm the only one in my year who plays the drums, so I'm often asked to play in performances. I'm going to university soon and I'm thinking about changing to a different instrument. I can't imagine ⁶_____ without music, but the drums are not easy enough to transport.

What about you? Do you play any musical instruments?

I can understand a post on a music blog.

4.4 Grammar

Quantifiers: *some, any, much, many, (a) few, (a) little, a lot of, lots of*

GRAMMAR › Quantifiers

Countable nouns	Uncountable nouns
I've got a lot of/lots of ideas. How many actors are there? There aren't many actors.	She's got a lot of/lots of style. How much money have we got? We haven't got much money.
There are some things we need to include. I haven't got any clothes. Have you got any ideas?	I've got some information. She hasn't got any make-up. Have you got any make-up?
I've written down a few things. There are very few people.	I only have a little make-up. We've got very little time.

1 ● Write the quantifiers below in the correct column.

(a) few   (a) little   a lot of   any   lots of
many   much   some

Countable nouns	Uncountable nouns	Countable and uncountable nouns
(a) few		

2 ● Choose the correct option.
1 How *much* / *many* channels have you got?
2 How *much* / *many* food do we need for the party?
3 I've got *some* / *any* new films to watch.
4 She doesn't have *some* / *any* jewellery to wear.
5 Are there *some* / *any* music shops in your town?
6 Tara has got *a little* / *a lot of* friends.

3 ● Match the sentence halves.
1 [c] Can you wait a few
2 [ ] Hurry up – we've got very little
3 [ ] There are very few
4 [ ] I can lend you a little
5 [ ] Have you got any
6 [ ] They've got some

a time before the show starts.
b money if you like.
c ~~minutes? I'm nearly ready.~~
d festivals in this area – only one or two.
e new information about the video challenge.
f ideas for a costume?

4 ●● Choose the correct answer.
A: Hi, Lottie. Would you like to see ¹___ photos from the film competition?
B: Oh yes, please. Is it a big competition? How ²___ people take part in it?
A: ³___ people! Look at my costume.
B: Wow! It's really colourful. Did you make it?
A: Yes. Look, here's Dean. He's made ⁴___ films before and had ⁵___ good ideas.
B: What's your film about?
A: It's a comedy about a band. It was actually quite stressful. We had very ⁶___ time to practise before we had to film it.
B: And do you have ⁷___ information about the winners yet?
A: No, not yet. I think the organisers need ⁸___ time to watch all the videos.

1 **a** some   b much   c few
2 a lots of   b a lot of   c many
3 a Much   b A little   c Lots of
4 a few   b a few   c any
5 a a lot of   b much   c any
6 a little   b a little   c few
7 a much   b few   c any
8 a little   b a lot of   c many

5 ●●● Complete the email with one word in each gap.

Hi Dan,

Do you want to come to a film-making course with me next weekend? I checked online and there are a ¹*few* places left. There are lots ²_____ good reviews about the course! On the first day there is information about costumes, make-up and about how to write a script. There is also ³_____ information about different cameras. Don't worry – you don't need ⁴_____ special equipment. On Sunday there is a ⁵_____ of information about editing and music. I don't know ⁶_____ about it, but I want to learn. I already have a ⁷_____ ideas for a short film.

See you soon, I hope!
Anita

Unit 4   42   I can talk about quantities.

On the Portal
Extra Practice Activities: Lesson 4.4

4.5 Listening and Vocabulary
The June Festival

1 Match the sentence halves.
1. **d** The festival celebrates all aspects of country
2. ___ We really enjoyed our summer
3. ___ I love carnival
4. ___ Many people enjoyed the traditional square
5. ___ I'm going to wear my new party

a dance at our local festival.
b dress on Saturday.
c holiday in Mexico.
d ~~life.~~
e music and all the colourful costumes.

2 Complete the sentences with compound nouns using one word from each box.

country	family	~~square~~	straw	summer

clothes	~~dance~~	hat	music	party

1. Some people got up to do a *square dance* when the music started.
2. Last winter we organised a big _____ to celebrate my grandad's birthday. About fifty of my relatives were there.
3. It's very hot in Spain, so bring plenty of _____ with you when you come to visit.
4. It was a hot day and Lily was wearing a _____ on her head.
5. I love dancing to _____. Everyone can join in!

3 🔊 4.1 Listen to part of a radio programme. Tick (✓) the events that are taking place during the festival.
1. ___ acting classes
2. ___ directing classes
3. ___ classes about designing costumes
4. ___ talks by actors
5. ___ opportunities to perform on stage
6. ___ theatre make-up workshops

4 🔊 4.2 Listen to Max and Jess talking about the festival. Choose the correct answer.
1. Why did Jess take part in this festival?
   a Her teacher recommended it.
   b Her friend Rosie invited her.
   c She enjoyed a drama lesson at school.
2. What did she learn about acting?
   a You use your face and your body to show your feelings.
   b It's best if you show your real feelings.
   c You have to show feelings very strongly.
3. What happened at lunchtime?
   a Jess felt ill.
   b A girl had an accident.
   c The teacher decided to play the main character.
4. What problem was there in the final show?
   a The music was too loud.
   b Some of the actors forgot their costumes.
   c The lights didn't work properly.
5. What did Jess enjoy the most?
   a the final show
   b singing on stage
   c meeting new people

5 🔊 4.2 Complete the sentences with the words below. Listen again and check.

comedy	lights	part	performances	teacher

1. Rosie always invites me to go to see unusual live _____ with her.
2. We've got this new drama _____ at school.
3. I guess you were good at it because you had a big _____ in the final show.
4. It was a _____ and the audience laughed a lot.
5. The only thing that went wrong was the stage _____.

I can understand a conversation about a festival.

4.6 Speaking
Talking about preferences

1 🔊 **4.3** Listen and repeat the phrases.

> **SPEAKING** — **Talking about preferences**
>
> **Asking about preferences**
> What would you rather do?
> Would you rather work in film or TV?
> What would you prefer to do?
> Would you prefer to work in film or TV?
>
> **Expressing preferences**
> I'd rather (not) go to the cinema.
> I'd prefer (not) to go to the theatre.
>
> **Giving reasons**
> It sounds funny/great/boring.
> It looks good.
> It's healthier.

2 Order the words to make sentences.
1. you / rather / on / Saturday / what / do / would / ?
   What would you rather do on Saturday?
2. prefer / go / to / I'd / shopping
   _____
3. film / this / very / sounds / funny
   _____
4. you / where / go / would / rather / on holiday / ?
   _____
5. tonight / prefer / what / do / to / you / would / ?
   _____
6. rather / I'd / film / at home / watch / a
   _____

3 Complete the sentences with the words below. There is one extra word.

> ~~healthier~~ look prefer rather (x2)
> sounds would

1. Let's have salad. It's *healthier*.
2. There are two comedies on. Which one would you _____ to see?
3. I'd _____ have something to eat first and then go to the cinema.
4. The festival _____ boring. I don't want to go.
5. Which event would you _____ go to this afternoon?
6. All the shows _____ great – it's difficult to choose.

4 Choose the correct response.
1. How was the music workshop?
   a   I'd prefer to do the dance workshop.
   (b) Great! I loved it!
   c   What would you rather do?
2. I'd rather see the puppet show.
   a   How was it?
   b   What would you prefer to see?
   c   OK. Cool! Let's do that.
3. Where would you rather eat?
   a   I'd prefer a pizza restaurant.
   b   No, thanks.
   c   OK. Cool!
4. I'd prefer to go to the photography class.
   a   Definitely the comedy workshop.
   b   Yeah, it sounds great.
   c   Why not?

5 🔊 **4.4** Complete the dialogue with sentences a–g. There is one extra sentence. Listen and check.

Mark: That was a great film. I'd like to be an actor one day.
Tamsin: Really? ¹*d*.
Mark: Why?
Tamsin: ² ____. You can make all the decisions.
Mark: That's true. But actors can be anyone they want. Hmm … Are you hungry?
Tamsin: Yes! But ³ ____, not at the cinema.
Mark: OK. I know two places we can go. ⁴ ____?
Tamsin: I've stopped eating meat, so no burgers for me. ⁵ ____.
Mark: That's good. ⁶ ____ too!

a   It's more interesting
b   Would you prefer to have pizza or burgers
c   It's tastier
d   ~~I'd prefer to be a director~~
e   Would you rather go to the cinema
f   Pizza sounds good
g   I'd rather eat in town

Unit 4 — 44 — I can talk about preferences.

On the Portal
Extra Practice Activities: Lesson 4.6

4.7 Writing
A review on a blog

1 Read the review. Match paragraphs 1–5 with topics a–e below.
- a ☐ Describing the performance
- b ☐ Starting your review
- c ☐ Ending your review
- d ☐ Describing the story
- e ☐ Ending your blog post

– THE NEW REVIEW BLOG –

Little Women

1. Today I'm going to tell you about a brilliant film I've just seen: *Little Women*. It's a 2019 film directed by Greta Gerwig.

2. The drama is based on a well-loved book by Louisa May Alcott and it tells the story of four sisters who are growing up in America. Life isn't easy for them, but they always help each other and never give up. It's a very inspiring story.

3. The actors all perform **brilliantly**. Saoirse Ronan is **particularly** good and I **really** liked the costumes. I usually choose films with a lot of special effects, but Little Women doesn't need any. It's still **extremely** good.

4. I **absolutely** love the book, but the film is also very **well** done. I **highly** recommend it to anyone who likes drama, romance and an amazing story. It's one of the best films of the year.

5. What's the best film you've seen **recently**? Write about it below.

2 Write the adverbs. Then check your answers in bold in the review.
1. brilliant — *brilliantly*
2. particular — _____
3. real — _____
4. extreme — _____
5. absolute — _____
6. good — _____
7. recent — _____
8. high — _____

3 Choose the correct option.
1. We saw the new drama starring Emma Watson (*recently*) / *absolutely*.
2. The music is *brilliantly* / *particularly* good.
3. The story is told *brilliantly* / *extremely*.
4. The performance was going *absolutely* / *well* until the lights went out.
5. The reviews were *absolutely* / *recently* terrible.

4 Match the sentence halves.
1. _b_ I've just seen a wonderful
2. ☐ You must see
3. ☐ It's the latest play
4. ☐ The story is about
5. ☐ The special effects

a. to open on Broadway.
b. ~~new comedy.~~
c. were amazing.
d. the new science fiction film.
e. a man who is lost in the desert.

WRITING TIME

5 Write an online review of a film or TV show based on a book.

1 Find ideas
Make notes about:
- where and when you saw it.
- what it was about.
- your opinions about it.

2 Plan and write
- Organise your ideas into paragraphs. Use the review of *Little Women* to help you.
- Write a draft review.

3 Check
- Check language: don't forget to use adjectives and adverbs?
- Check grammar: did you use comparatives, superlatives and quantifiers correctly?
- Write the final version of your review.

I can write a review on a blog.

My Language File

WORDLIST 🔊 4.5

Types of film
- action (n) _____
- cartoon (n) _____
- comedy (n) _____
- documentary (n) _____
- drama (n) _____
- musical (n) _____
- romance (n) _____
- science fiction (n) _____
- thriller (n) _____

Word building (entertainment)
- act (v) _____
- acting (n) _____
- actor (n) _____
- entertain (v) _____
- entertainer (n) _____
- entertainment (n) _____
- perform (v) _____
- performance (n) _____
- performer (n) _____
- produce (v) _____
- producer (n) _____
- production (n) _____
- review (v, n) _____
- reviewer (n) _____

Film and TV
- audience (n) _____
- channel (n) _____
- character (n) _____
- episode (n) _____
- hit (n) _____
- series (n) _____
- special effects (n) _____
- TV show (n) _____
- viewer (n) _____

Word friends (music)
- download a playlist _____
- go to a live performance _____
- lip-synch to music videos _____
- livestream an event _____
- record a track _____
- sing along to songs _____
- stream music _____
- write lyrics _____

Compound nouns
- carnival dress (n) _____
- country music (n) _____
- family holiday (n) _____
- family party (n) _____
- party dress (n) _____
- square dance (n) _____
- straw hat (n) _____
- summer holiday (n) _____

Extra words
- 4-D experience (n) _____
- album (n) _____
- animated film (n) _____
- based on (adj) _____
- biographical (adj) _____
- carnival (n) _____
- celebrate (v) _____
- challenge (n) _____
- check out (v) _____
- collect (v) _____
- costume (n) _____
- dialogue (n) _____
- dramatic (adj) _____
- drummer (n) _____
- exciting (adj) _____
- fantastic (adj) _____
- film festival (n) _____
- get a part _____
- guitarist (n) _____
- headphones (n) _____
- interview (n) _____
- location (n) _____
- main character (n) _____
- make-up (n) _____
- musician (n) _____
- old-fashioned (adj) _____
- personal (adj) _____
- programme (n) _____
- proud (adj) _____
- radio station (n) _____
- reaction (n) _____
- record player (n) _____
- romantic comedy (n) _____
- scary (adj) _____
- scene (n) _____
- seat (n) _____
- spectacular (adj) _____
- stage (n) _____
- star (n) _____
- style (n) _____
- successful (adj) _____
- talent (n) _____
- theatre (n) _____
- voice (n) _____
- wonderful (adj) _____

Sounds good!
- You're in the right place. _____
- I can read your mind. _____

MY LANGUAGE NOTES

My favourite words/expressions from this unit

Self-check

Vocabulary

1 Complete the words in the sentences.
1 We watched a brilliant s_____ f_____ film about people building a city on Mars.
2 *Inside Out* is a c_____. The characters are drawings, not real people.
3 All the reviewers agree that she gave a very good p_____ in the film.
4 Who plays the main c_____ in the film?
5 The show was a big h___ in the USA.
6 The a_____ clapped loudly at the end of the show.
7 I find a_____ films quite stressful with so many fights and explosions. Let's watch a comedy.
8 Let's watch one more e_____. I have to find out what happens next!

2 Order the letters and complete the words in the sentences.
1 Many teenagers s_____ (RETMAS) music instead of downloading it.
2 The band wants to r_____ (DORREC) a track this weekend.
3 Jennifer is very good at writing l_____ (SCRILY).
4 I'm going to download a p_____ (LIYLAPST) for my friend's birthday party.
5 I often sing a_____ (GAOLN) to songs in the car.
6 Did you go to the live p_____ (MAREPFORCEN) last weekend?

3 Complete the sentences with the words below.

dance   family   hat   holiday   music   party

1 I'm looking forward to spending my summer _____ lying on a beach.
2 We are organising a big _____ party to celebrate my dad's birthday.
3 You can do a square _____ to this music.
4 I love your straw _____!
5 You look lovely in your _____ dress!
6 The carnival _____ always makes me want to dance.

Grammar

4 Complete the second sentence so that it means the same as the first sentence. Use no more than three words.
1 Documentaries aren't as popular as comedies.
Comedies are _____ documentaries.
2 The seats in the theatre weren't big enough.
The seats in the theatre _____ small.
3 No one in our class is as tall as Paul.
Paul is _____ in our class.
4 The film is more expensive than the book.
The book isn't _____ the film.
5 I've never seen a better play than this one.
This is _____ I've ever seen.
6 You're too young to go to the concert.
You aren't _____ to go to the concert.
7 The second part isn't as good as the first part.
The first part is _____ the second part.
8 Janet is the youngest contestant in the show.
Everyone is _____ Janet in the show.

5 Choose the correct option.
1 How *much / many* people went on the trip?
2 Jake's got *many / lots of* money!
3 I'm sorry I haven't got *some / any* apple juice.
4 There isn't *much / many* food left.
5 I've seen *a few / a little* good films this year.
6 My dad gets very *a little / little* time off work.
7 I have got *any / some* ideas for the video.

Speaking

6 Complete the dialogues with the phrases below.

I'd prefer   I'd rather   it sounds   looks better   would you prefer

1 A: Shall we go to the cinema tonight?
B: _____ watch a film at home.
A: OK. Shall we watch that new comedy?
B: Yeah, _____ very funny.
2 A: Which one _____ to see?
B: _____ to see the musical.
A: I agree. It _____ than the thriller.

YOUR SCORE

Vocabulary: __/20   Speaking: __/5
Grammar: __/15   Total: __/40

To the limit

VOCABULARY
Sports equipment | Sporting events | Sports collocations | Fitness and training | Word building: sport

GRAMMAR
Future forms: *will*, *be going to*, Present Continuous and Present Simple | First Conditional with *if* and *unless*

5.1 Vocabulary
Sport

1 ● Match words 1–10 with pictures A–J.

1	B	basketball	6		skateboard
2		football kit	7		skates
3		life jacket	8		snorkel
4		mask	9		snowboard
5		net	10		surfboard

2 ●● Read the descriptions. Complete the names of the sports equipment.

1 You can wear this to breathe underwater. s*norkel*
2 You wear this to protect your head when skiing, climbing and cycling. h_____
3 You attach these to your feet to move quickly down a mountain. s_____
4 You can lie on this to do exercise. m_____
5 You use this to hit the ball in cricket and baseball. b_____
6 You wear this to play football. f_____ k_____
7 You use this to play tennis. r_____
8 You wear these to help you to move quickly through water. f_____

3 ● Order the letters to make words and complete the sentences.

1 I put my kit on in the c*hanging* (NACHGNIG) room before the game.
2 Wow, I didn't know that tennis c_____ (ROCUTS) were so big! Players have to run a lot!
3 My next o_____ (NEPOPONT) in the karate competition is very strong.
4 There were over 50,000 people in the s_____ (MITADUS) for the big match.
5 Our school has just got a new running t_____ (CRATK). It's great for our training.
6 At the end of the game, the s_____ (ROADRECOBS) showed 12–8 to my team!

4 ●● Complete the dialogue with the words below. There is one extra word.

> changing room   fans   opponent   pitch   scoreboard   ~~stadium~~   tournament

A: Wow! That was a really exciting football match. I love the new ¹*stadium*! I'm glad our team won in the end.
B: Yes. I was a bit worried at half time when the ²_____ showed 1–0 to the other team, but then Juan Fernandez got that amazing goal!
A: Yes. That gave our players a lot of confidence. And the ³_____ all got really excited when he scored another one!
B: Yeah. A few people tried to run onto the ⁴_____ to celebrate, but of course, you aren't allowed to do that!
A: Of course not. Anyway, I think the teams in this year's ⁵_____ are much stronger than last year.
B: I agree. Who is our next ⁶_____?
A: I don't know. It depends who wins the other match.

5 **WORD FRIENDS** Match the sentence halves.

1. [d] I think we're going to win
2. [ ] I've decided to take
3. [ ] We have to beat
4. [ ] I don't support
5. [ ] We're taking part
6. [ ] John holds
7. [ ] How many goals
8. [ ] I volunteer

a this team to stay in the tournament.
b any football team at the moment.
c up gymnastics.
d ~~this game.~~
e the school record for the high jump.
f in a badminton competition this weekend.
g at sports events after school.
h did they score yesterday?

6 Choose the correct answer.

1. Ben ___ the record for throwing the ball the furthest.
   a) holds   b wins   c scores
2. It's important to wear ___ when you go kayaking.
   a flippers   b a life jacket   c a mask
3. Last year I ___ at the local golf club and I met some famous golfers.
   a supported   b broke   c volunteered
4. Look at the ___! We're winning!
   a scoreboard   b tournament   c stadium
5. I need to put on my football kit. Where is the ___?
   a court   b event   c changing room
6. When does the swimming ___ start?
   a club   b track   c tournament
7. I love the new football ___. Blue is my favourite colour.
   a track   b kit   c fan

7 Choose the correct option.

1. I want to (take) / get up a new sport this year.
2. Do you want to volunteer / support at the tennis club with me?
3. Has your team ever held / won a match?
4. I'm taking place / part in a race tomorrow morning.
5. She beat / played her opponent easily.
6. How do you feel when you take / score a goal?
7. I'd love to win / break the school record in the 100-metre run.

8 Complete the comments about sports with one word in each gap.

Snowboarding is a really exciting sport. You need a ¹ snowboard to stand on and a ² _____ for your head. You also need warm clothes. Then you are ready to have fun in the mountains!

I started doing yoga a few years ago. It's so relaxing and you don't need any special equipment, only a ³ _____ to lie on. I'm not interested in competitions or breaking ⁴ _____, so it's the perfect sport for me.

I love all competitive sports. The best feeling is beating an ⁵ _____. I ⁶ _____ part in as many competitions as possible!

I don't do many sports myself, but I'm a big football ⁷ _____. I ⁸ _____ my local team and I always know what the latest scores are.

I can talk about sports equipment and sporting events.

On the Portal
Extra Practice Activities: Lesson 5.1

5.2 Grammar
Future forms: *will*, *be going to*, Present Continuous, Present Simple

GRAMMAR — Future forms

Predictions or decisions made at the moment of speaking
I**'ll do** it!
I **won't be** able to finish.
Will that **help** me run 5K? Yes, it **will**.

Plans and predictions based on things we know now
It**'s going to rain** all week.
Are you really **going to run** five kilometres?

Arrangements
I**'m doing** the 5K Fun Run next month.

Timetables
It **starts** in ten minutes.

1 ● Match the verbs in bold in sentences 1–6 with functions a–f.
1. [c] Off you go. I'm sure you**'ll have** fun.
2. [   ] Don't worry, I**'ll do** the washing-up.
3. [   ] I**'m meeting** Sam this afternoon.
4. [   ] I**'m going to take** up a new sport this year!
5. [   ] Look – it**'s going to rain**.
6. [   ] The match **starts** at 7.30.

a an arrangement
b a timetable
c ~~a prediction made at the moment of speaking~~
d a prediction based on what we know now
e a decision made at the moment of speaking
f a plan

2 ● Choose the correct option.
1. They're a very good team – I think (**they'll win**) / they win today.
2. Hurry up – the race *starts* / *will start* in fifteen minutes!
3. Is your bag heavy? Wait, *I'm going to help* / *I'll help* you.
4. *I'll go* / *I'm going* on holiday on Saturday.
5. Freddie *will join* / *is going to join* a gym so he can do more training.
6. Be careful on that ladder – *you're going to fall* / *you fall*.

3 ●● Read the dialogue. Choose the correct answer.
A: Hi, James. What are your plans for the weekend?
B: Well, ¹____ football on Saturday afternoon.
A: Really? What time ²____ the match start?
B: At three o'clock.
A: Cool! ³____ and watch.
B: Great! I think it ⁴____ an exciting match.
A: Good. What about later? Have you got any plans?
B: Yes, Ali ⁵____ me after the match. He wants to go to the cinema in the evening. Do you want to come with us?
A: Sorry, I can't. ⁶____ dinner with my grandparents at eight o'clock. Maybe next week.

1 a I play   (b) I'm playing   c I will play
2 a will   b is   c does
3 a I'll come   b I come   c I'm coming
4 a is   b will be   c is being
5 a calls   b is going to call   c won't call
6 a I'm having   b I'll have   c I have

4 ●●● Choose the correct option.

Hi. Mia ¹*comes* / (*is coming*) round to my house this evening to watch the match. Do you want to come?

What ²*will you watch* / *are you going to watch*?

It's a tennis match. I think ³*you enjoy* / *you'll enjoy* it. The two players are excellent.

Sounds great. My fitness class ⁴*finishes* / *will finish* at 5.30, so I can come after that.

Great! Mia ⁵*is going to order* / *orders* some pizzas too.

Cool! So ⁶*I'm going to bring* / *I'll bring* some snacks with me.

Great! See you later.

Unit 5 — 50 — I can talk about plans, predictions, arrangements and timetables.

On the Portal
Extra Practice Activities: Lesson 5.2

5.3 Reading and Vocabulary
Sports and hobbies

1 Read the article quickly. Tick (✓) which sports are mentioned.
- [ ] basketball
- [ ] tennis
- [ ] climbing
- [ ] yoga
- [ ] handball

Is PE an important subject?

Is PE as important as other subjects such as Maths, foreign languages or Science? Let's find out!

Miles, 15
Three years ago, I decided to take up climbing. Climbers need to have excellent strength and good balance; two skills that we need in life. I believe it's important for all teenagers to do some exercise, but not everyone wants to do sport in their free time. So, we definitely need to have PE lessons at school. Why is sport important? When I don't work out, I feel stressed and I can't concentrate on my schoolwork. PE lessons help everyone to learn new skills, relax and stop worrying about exams, homework and other problems.

Li, 16
My favourite subjects at school are Maths and Science, but I also enjoy PE lessons. I don't like team sports like volleyball or handball, but I think jogging and yoga are OK. Some of my friends hate PE and would rather spend the time doing homework or revising for exams, but I'm not sure. I have learned some important things in PE, for example how to warm up and stretch so that I don't get hurt. I think everyone should do some sport at school, but we should choose how many PE lessons we have each week.

James, 14
I know that sport is good for the body and mind, but PE lessons are a nightmare. I get really stressed when I can't focus on the things that I am good at, like Maths. Spending hours on a cold football pitch is such a waste of time. And I don't think we learn anything. The kids who are good at sport have fun, and everyone else just waits for it to finish. It is important for everyone to work out, but we can do that in the gym, in the park or at home. So I think we should have PE lessons after school.

2 Read the article again and for each question write: Miles, Li or James.
1 Who thinks PE lessons don't give students new skills? _____
2 Who has problems studying when they don't do exercise? _____
3 Who mentions that they like PE lessons? _____
4 Who thinks PE lessons shouldn't be part of the normal school day? _____
5 Who talks about new skills that students can learn in PE lessons? _____
6 Who says that working out helps them to forget about their problems? _____
7 Who thinks students should decide how many PE lessons to have? _____

3 Choose the correct option.
1 We should warm *up* / *down* before the match.
2 Are you following a *programme* / *balance* to get fit?
3 I'm looking for a new tennis *strength* / *coach*.
4 I lost my *balance* / *stretch* when I was standing on one leg.
5 She has such good football *skills* / *exercises*.
6 I'm working on improving my *programme* / *strength*.

4 Complete the sentences with the words below.

| exercises | practise | programme | stretch |
| warm | ~~work~~ | | |

1 How many times a week do you *work* out?
2 What is the best way to _____ up before doing sport?
3 Can you show me how to _____ my legs properly?
4 I'm going to _____ my dance routine this evening.
5 This website has lots of great _____ you can do at home with no equipment.
6 The training _____ includes running, yoga and swimming.

I can understand an article about fitness and training.

5.4 Grammar

First Conditional with *if* and *unless*

GRAMMAR — First Conditional with *if* and *unless*

You **won't know** if you **don't try**!
You **won't know** unless you **try**!

Time clauses with *when* follow a similar pattern.
When I**'m** back home, I**'ll watch** some slacklining videos.

1 ● Choose the correct option.
1 *You enjoy* / (*You'll enjoy*) gymnastics if *you try* / *you'll try* it.
2 If *you have* / *you'll have* some skiing lessons, *you be* / *you'll be* a very good skier.
3 We *don't go* / *won't go* for a walk unless the weather *is* / *will be* good.
4 *You get* / *You'll get* fitter if *you join* / *you'll join* a gym.
5 You *don't improve* / *won't improve* unless you *practise* / *you'll practise*.

2 ● Complete the sentences with *if* or *unless*.
1 We'll go to the match *unless* the tickets are too expensive.
2 He won't get strong _____ he doesn't do any exercise.
3 We'll play outside _____ it starts to rain.
4 They won't let you in _____ you have a ticket.
5 They won't cancel the game _____ the weather isn't too bad.

3 ●● Complete the dialogue with the correct form of the verbs in brackets.
A: Do you want to come ice skating with me on Saturday?
B: Er, I haven't got any skates.
A: I'm sure Jenna ¹*will lend* (lend) you hers if you ² _____ (ask) her.
B: But I'm worried I ³ _____ (hurt) myself if I ⁴ _____ (fall) over.
A: Don't worry. You ⁵ _____ (not get) injured if you ⁶ _____ (be) careful.
B: But sometimes there are loads of people there.
A: Well, if it ⁷ _____ (be) very busy when we get there, we ⁸ _____ (wait) until it's quieter. We ⁹ _____ (not go) on the ice unless you ¹⁰ _____ (feel) it's safe.
B: OK. Why not? I'll give it a go!

4 ●● Complete the second sentence so that it means the same as the first sentence. Use no more than three words.
1 We won't go climbing unless it's sunny.
   We *will go* climbing if it's sunny.
2 I'll pay for lunch if it isn't too expensive.
   I'll pay for lunch _____ is too expensive.
3 Our holiday won't be any fun if the weather isn't good.
   Our holiday will be fun _____ is good.
4 You won't become a great slackliner unless you practise every day.
   You won't become a great slackliner if _____ practise every day.
5 We'll be there at three o'clock if our train is on time.
   We'll be there at three o'clock _____ is late.

5 ●●● Choose the correct answer.

So, my climbing adventure starts today! I've got my first lesson at the climbing centre in my town. I'm feeling a bit nervous, but I know that the instructors will help me ¹____ have any problems. I'll start on the junior climbing wall and I'll have a rope on, so I won't get hurt ²____ fall. There are three higher walls, but the instructors probably won't let me climb them ³____ think I'm ready. My aunt does loads of climbing and she says that ⁴____ enjoy it, she'll take me climbing with her in the mountains. But I won't go with her ⁵____ feel really confident. Climbing can be a dangerous sport! Well, I must go now. My lesson starts at two, so I have to leave soon.

1 a if I'll   (b) if I
  c unless I
2 a if I   b if I'll
  c unless I
3 a if they won't   b unless they
  c if they
4 a unless I   b if I'll
  c if I
5 a unless I   b if I won't
  c if I'll

I can use the First Conditional to talk about possible situations in the future.

On the Portal
Extra Practice Activities: Lesson 5.4

5.5 Listening and Vocabulary
A young tennis player

1 WORD BUILDING Choose the correct option.
1. Only the *win* / *winner* will go to the next round of the competition.
2. That was a really good *attack* / *attacker* by the other team.
3. I'd love to be a sports *management* / *manager* one day.
4. They are going to *present* / *presenter* the prizes this evening.
5. They are playing so badly. They didn't *defend* / *defence* the goal at all.

2 WORD BUILDING Complete the sentences with the correct form of the words in brackets.
1. They do three hours of *training* (TRAIN) every week.
2. Rob _____ (PRACTICE) his football skills every day.
3. Stella is a really good tennis _____ (PLAY).
4. Do you want to enter the _____ (RACE) with me?
5. All the _____ (SUPPORT) were happy about the result.
6. My uncle works as a sports _____ (COACH).
7. Who _____ (SCORE) the winning goal in last week's match?

3 🔊 5.1 Listen to a report. Mark the sentences T (true) or F (false).
1. ___ Anna Martin is good at her sport.
2. ___ Anna Martin hasn't won many matches recently.
3. ___ Anna Martin is planning to work as a coach.

4 🔊 5.2 Listen to Angela and Paul talking about Anna Martin and choose the correct answer.
1. What does Angela think about the news about Anna Martin?
   a She expected it.
   b She's surprised.
   c She thinks it's a good plan.
2. Paul thinks that it's better for Anna Martin
   a to focus on doing something that she enjoys.
   b to study how to be a good coach.
   c to train hard every day.
3. How many hours does Anna Martin spend practising tennis every day?
   a two
   b three
   c four
4. Angela thinks Anna Martin will
   a make a lot of money as a coach.
   b spend more time with her brother.
   c be popular with young players.
5. Anna Martin
   a is already working with future tennis stars.
   b wants to help future stars to do charity work.
   c is planning to give more of her money to charity.

5 🔊 5.2 Complete the sentences with the words below. Listen again and check.

| changes | giving | point | raises | role |

1. I can't believe she's _____ up playing.
2. I hope she _____ her mind.
3. She plays in lots of charity matches and _____ a lot of money.
4. There's no _____ in training all day every day if you don't enjoy it.
5. She also wants to be a _____ model for them.

I can understand a conversation about sports personalities.

On the Portal
Extra Practice Activities: Lesson 5.5

5.6 Speaking
Talking about plans

1 🔊 **5.3** Listen and repeat the phrases.

> **SPEAKING — Talking about plans**
>
> **Asking**
> What are you up to today/at the weekend?
> Have you got any plans for this evening/tomorrow?
> What are you doing on Sunday/next Saturday?
>
> **Answering and following up**
> I'm/We're visiting my grandma/going to the cinema.
> First I'm going to a soccer match.
> I'm going to help a friend.
> Then/After that/Later we're going to the cinema.
> I don't have any plans.   I don't know yet.
> What about you?   And you?   What are your plans?

2 Match the sentence halves.

1. [c] What are you up
2. [ ] I don't have
3. [ ] Have you got any
4. [ ] I'm visiting my
5. [ ] What are you
6. [ ] I'm going to

a doing tonight?
b grandparents on Sunday.
c ~~to on Saturday?~~
d help you.
e any plans yet.
f plans for the weekend?

3 Complete the dialogue with the words below.

| about | after | ~~first~~ | know | then | what |

Alex: What are you doing at the weekend, Laura?
Laura: ¹*First* of all I'm going shopping on Saturday morning. ²_____ that I'm meeting some friends for lunch. What ³_____ you? What are you doing?
Alex: I don't ⁴_____ what I'm doing yet. And you, Sam? ⁵_____ are your plans?
Sam: I'm going swimming in the morning. ⁶_____ I'm going to a football match.

4 Choose the correct response.

1. What are you up to this evening?
   a And you?
   (b) I don't know yet.
   c Great!
2. I'm going swimming on Saturday. What about you?
   a I don't have any plans yet.
   b Later I'm going shopping.
   c Yes, OK.
3. I'm going to a concert this weekend.
   a I don't know yet.
   b And you?
   c That's nice.
4. First I'm going to my tennis lesson.
   a What are your plans?
   b Cool. Have you got any plans after that?
   c What about you?

5 🔊 **5.4** Complete the dialogue with the words below. There are two extra words. Listen and check.

| about | after | ~~any~~ | could | doing | first |
| great | plans | then | you | | |

Jen: Have you got ¹*any* plans for Saturday?
Leo: Yes, I've got quite a busy day. ²_____ of all, I'm going to football training, as usual, and ³_____ that I'm going karting with my uncle. Have you ever done it? You drive these little mini racing cars round a race track.
Jen: That sounds cool!
Leo: Yeah. What ⁴_____ you? What are you ⁵_____ on Saturday?
Jen: We're visiting my cousin in the morning. ⁶_____ I'll probably do my homework in the afternoon.
Leo: You ⁷_____ come karting with me instead.
Jen: Wow. That would be ⁸_____! Thanks! I can do my homework on Sunday.

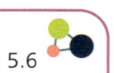

I can ask and talk about plans.

On the Portal
Extra Practice Activities: Lesson 5.6

5.7 Writing
Short messages

1 Match messages A–C with the correct reason for writing below.
1. ☐ Congratulating someone
2. ☐ Asking for something
3. ☐ Thanking someone

A
Hey Ahmed,
Just a quick note to thank you for helping me to find my skis before the race on Saturday. I can't believe I left them at the bus stop! I was so nervous about the competition that I completely forgot about everything else! Would you like to take part in the next competition? I can help you to train, if you want.
See you later,
Pierre

B
Hi Team,
Congratulations on doing a great job at the race last weekend. If we train hard, we might win a medal in the next round. Let's meet next weekend to set up a training programme. Would it be possible to meet somewhere on Saturday morning? Is the park all right for everybody?
Cheers,
Holly

C
Hi there Gabriella,
Would you mind buying some snacks for the football practice tomorrow? How about some apples or bananas? The team will be hungry after training so maybe some nuts too. I'll give you the money tomorrow.
Let me know if that's OK.
Bye,
Claudia

2 Read the messages again and for each question write: Holly, Ahmed, Pierre or Claudia.
1. Who asks someone to buy food?
   _____
2. Who offers to help someone train?
   _____
3. Who thinks the team can win an event in the future? _____
4. Who looked for something that was lost?
   _____

3 Complete the sentences with the words and phrases below. Then check your ideas in the messages.

<del>a quick note</del>   later   me know if   on doing
would it be   you mind buying

1. Just *a quick note* to thank you for helping me.
2. Congratulations _____ a great job.
3. See you _____.
4. _____ possible to meet somewhere on Saturday morning?
5. Would _____ a few snacks?
6. Let _____ that's OK.

4 Complete the sentences with the prepositions below.

after   before   <del>for</del>   on   to

1. Thanks *for* helping me.
2. I was excited _____ the match, but it was boring.
3. I was sad _____ my team lost the competition.
4. I'm looking forward _____ seeing you soon.
5. I'd like to congratulate you _____ beating your opponent.

WRITING TIME

5 Write three short messages: to thank someone, to congratulate someone and to make a request. Follow the instructions below.

Thanking someone for …	Congratulating someone for …	Asking someone to …
• giving you a present	• winning a sports event	• look after your pet
• helping you with schoolwork	• organising a charity event	• teach you a new skill

1 Find ideas
Make notes about:
- who you want to write to.
- why you are writing to them.

2 Plan and write
- Organise your ideas into three short messages. Use the messages in Exercise 1 to help you.
- Write draft messages.

3 Check
- Check language: did you use the *-ing* form after prepositions?
- Check grammar: did you use future forms correctly?
- Write the final version of your messages.

I can write a short message to thank, congratulate and make a request.

My Language File

WORDLIST 🔊 5.5

Sports equipment
- basketball (n) _____
- bat (n) _____
- flippers (n) _____
- football kit (n) _____
- helmet (n) _____
- life jacket (n) _____
- mask (n) _____
- mat (n) _____
- net (n) _____
- racket (n) _____
- skateboard (n) _____
- skates (n) _____
- skis (n) _____
- snorkel (n) _____
- snowboard (n) _____
- surfboard (n) _____

Sporting events
- changing room (n) _____
- court (n) _____
- fan (n) _____
- opponent (n) _____
- pitch (n) _____
- scoreboard (n) _____
- stadium (n) _____
- tournament (n) _____
- track (n) _____

Word friends (sports)
- beat a team _____
- beat an opponent _____
- break a record _____
- hold a record _____
- score a goal _____
- support a team _____
- take part in a competition _____
- take part in a race _____
- take up a sport _____
- volunteer at a club _____
- volunteer at a sports event _____
- win a game _____
- win a match _____
- win a medal _____

Fitness and training
- balance (n) _____
- coach (n) _____
- exercise (n) _____
- practise (v) _____
- skill (n) _____
- strength (n) _____
- stretch (v) _____
- training programme (n) _____
- warm down (v) _____
- warm up (v) _____
- work out (v) _____

Word building (sport)
- attack (v, n) _____
- attacker (n) _____
- coach (v, n) _____
- coaching (n) _____
- defence (n) _____
- defend (v) _____
- defender (n) _____
- manage (v) _____
- management (n) _____
- manager (n) _____
- practice (n) _____
- practise (v) _____
- score (v, n) _____
- scorer (n) _____
- support (v, n) _____
- supporter (n) _____
- train (v) _____
- trainer (n) _____
- training (n) _____

Extra words
- award (n) _____
- badminton (n) _____
- baseball (n) _____
- champion (n) _____
- charity (n) _____
- compete (v) _____
- competition (n) _____
- competitive (adj) _____
- Congratulations! _____
- cricket (n) _____
- encourage (v) _____
- event (n) _____
- fitness (n) _____
- follow (v) _____
- ice hockey (n) _____
- kayaking (n) _____
- keep fit _____
- professional (n) _____
- race (n) _____
- rink (n) _____
- rope (n) _____
- rugby (n) _____
- sailing (n) _____
- skipping (n) _____
- spin (v) _____
- sports personality (n) _____
- sports centre (n) _____
- success (n) _____
- trick (n) _____
- yoga (n) _____

Sounds good!
- Nothing special. _____
- Can you make it? _____

MY LANGUAGE NOTES

My favourite words/expressions from this unit

_____
_____
_____
_____
_____
_____
_____

Self-check

Vocabulary

1 Choose the correct answer.
1. We couldn't play football because the ___ was too wet.
   a track   b pitch   c opponent
2. My basketball team wear a red and white ___.
   a kit   b mask   c net
3. The ___ all cheered when she scored.
   a court   b track   c fans
4. The final result on the ___ was 4–2.
   a scoreboard   b stadium   c bat
5. I'd like to ___ at the Olympics.
   a volunteer   b break   c support
6. Do you ___ part in competitions?
   a play   b take   c go
7. I do water sports – I just bought a new ___.
   a mat   b racket   c life jacket
8. How fast did she run when she ___ the world record?
   a scored   b won   c broke

2 Choose the correct option.
1. After we train, we always *warm up / warm down*.
2. It's important to find a good *coach / skill* if you want to improve.
3. How often do you *programme / exercise*?
4. All athletes should *stretch / strength* to stay healthy.
5. Dancers need to have good *stretch / balance*.
6. I'm trying a new exercise *practise / programme* to get strong.

3 Complete the sentences with the correct form of the word in bold.
1. The ___ were very excited after the match. **SUPPORT**
2. My sister is a ___ in the local football team. **DEFENCE**
3. Come on, we'll be late for our football ___. **PRACTISE**
4. Do you think we'll ___ another goal before half time? **SCORER**
5. The ___ really hurt his foot. I hope he's OK. **PLAY**
6. Who do you think will be the new ___? **MANAGE**

Grammar

4 Complete the sentences with the verbs below.

'll pay   'll win   'm going to take up   'm meeting
opens   're training   's going to score

1. The library ___ at 9 tomorrow.
2. I'm sure you ___ the match tomorrow.
3. Look, Messi's got the ball – he ___!
4. I ___ tennis next summer.
5. The film starts at eight. I ___ Tina at half past seven.
6. No, don't give me any money. I ___ for the tickets.
7. We ___ in the park later.

5 Complete the sentences with the correct form of the verbs in brackets.
1. I ___ fitter if I ___ sport. (get/do)
2. If you ___ regularly, you ___ into the team. (not practise/not get)
3. You ___ the race unless you ___ fast. (not win/run)
4. If it ___, we ___ table tennis indoors. (rain/play)
5. You ___ your head if you ___ a helmet. (not hurt/wear)
6. I ___ at four o'clock tomorrow unless my train ___ late. (arrive/be)
7. You ___ tired if you ___ to bed earlier. (not be/go)
8. If you ___ flippers, you ___ faster. (buy/swim)

Speaking

6 Complete the dialogues with the words and phrases below.

don't know   first   got any plans   up to   what about

1. A: What are you ___ at the weekend?
   B: Staying at home probably. ___ you?
   A: I ___ yet.
2. A: Have you ___ for Saturday?
   B: Yeah. ___, I'm going into town.

YOUR SCORE

Vocabulary: __/20   Speaking: __/5
Grammar: __/15   Total: __/40

Explore more

VOCABULARY
Types of holidays | Going on holiday | Holiday equipment and accommodation | Traffic and transport | Travel: confusing words

GRAMMAR
Modal verbs: *must, have to, ought to, should* | Modal verbs: *must, could, may/might, can't*

6   6.1   Vocabulary
Holidays and travel

1 ● Read the comments and order the letters to make the type of holiday each person wants.

1 I'd love to visit some of the monuments in ancient Egypt. s<u>ightseeing</u> h<u>oliday</u> (NEEGISHTSIG LAYODIH)
2 I'd like to go to Paris for a weekend. c_____ b_____ (TICY KERAB)
3 My dream holiday would be to spend two weeks on a ship, visiting different places. o_____ c_____ (ACOEN URICES)
4 I just want to lie in the sun and swim in the sea! b_____ h_____ (EBACH OHILYAD)
5 I enjoy sleeping in a tent and spending time outdoors. c_____ t_____ (PIMAGCN PRIT)
6 I'd love to travel around Europe with a friend, with just our bags on our backs and no real plan! b_____ h_____ (CKABAKPICNG YOLIDAH)
7 I like doing different sports and outdoor activities with other young people. a_____ c_____ (VITYICAT MACP)

2 ● **WORD FRIENDS** Match the sentence halves.

1 [c] Do you want to eat
2 [ ] My grandparents are going
3 [ ] Last summer we stayed
4 [ ] We can book
5 [ ] My sister is travelling around
6 [ ] I've never travelled by
7 [ ] My parents usually rent

a on a cruise this summer.
b a hotel online.
c ~~out this evening?~~
d Europe. I'm so jealous.
e plane.
f on a campsite and it rained every day!
g a holiday flat when we travel.

3 ●● Complete the sentences with the words below.

| abroad | around | ~~break~~ | flat | off | train |

1 We are going to have a city *break* after we finish our exams.
2 My parents rented a very nice holiday _____ in Italy.
3 We have to get _____ the bus. It's our stop!
4 I want to go _____ next summer to learn something about a different culture.
5 I don't like travelling by _____. There are usually too many people.
6 You need a lot of money to go _____ the world.

4 ● Look at pictures 1–6 and complete the words.

1 s<u>w</u> <u>i</u> m <u>s</u> <u>u</u> <u>i</u> <u>t</u>   2 r_____ / b_____

3 t_____   4 s_____

5 g_____   6 t_____

Unit 6   58

5 ●● Write the correct word for each definition.
1. You use this to find out about places to visit on holiday. g*uidebook*
2. You use this to see what a place looks like. It shows things like streets, rivers and lakes. m_____
3. You put this on your skin, so you don't burn in the sun. s_____ c_____
4. You sleep in this when you go camping. s_____ b_____
5. You wear these to protect your eyes from the sun. s_____
6. You show this to officials when you enter a country. p_____

6 ●● Complete the review with the words below.

check out   facilities   floor   guests   pool
~~reception~~   reservation   single   view

4.0 Very good

This is a great hotel. The staff at the ¹*reception* desk were really friendly. I made my ²_____ online. I was travelling on my own, so I had a ³_____ room. Ask for a room at the front of the hotel and on the top ⁴_____ – they're a bit more expensive, but worth it for the ⁵_____ of the beach. There's a ⁶_____ where you can swim, but there are 300 ⁷_____ in the hotel, so it's often quite busy. Other ⁸_____ include a gym and a spa where you can relax. Be careful: on the day you leave, you have to ⁹_____ by ten o'clock. If you're late, they'll charge you for another day!

7 ●●● Complete the adverts with one word in each gap.

Global Holidays

THIS WEEK'S SPECIAL OFFERS

Seven days on the Mediterranean

A seven-day ocean ¹*cruise* on a luxury ship. Travelling ²_____ sea is always relaxing and it's even better when the ship has fantastic ³_____ like three cinemas and twelve different restaurants. Each morning explore ⁴_____ foot, before setting sail for the next exciting destination.

£1,400 per person

A long weekend in New York

New York is a great place for a city ⁵_____. Enjoy the atmosphere of one of the world's great cities. You will stay in a double ⁶_____ in a downtown hotel and eat ⁷_____ in some of New York's best restaurants.

£1,250 per person

A great value beach holiday

Spend six days lying on golden sands or swimming in clear blue seas on Kefalonia, a popular Greek island. Stay in a luxury hotel with a heated outdoor ⁸_____ and an amazing restaurant serving real Greek food. All rooms have fantastic ⁹_____ over the sea. You can also ¹⁰_____ sightseeing in nearby villages.

£850 per person

I can talk about holidays and travel.

6.2 Grammar

Modal verbs: *must, have to, ought to, should*

GRAMMAR — Modal verbs: *must, have to, ought to, should*

Obligation and prohibition
You **must** be careful.
Do we **have to** sleep on the boat?
You **mustn't** do anything silly.

Advice
You **ought to** take these to help you swim.
You **shouldn't** forget your swimsuit.

Lack of obligation
You **don't have to** wear a life jacket.

1 ● Order the words to make sentences.
1. must / wear / life jacket / you / a
   <u>You must wear a life jacket.</u>
2. don't / we / pay / parking / have / for / to
   _____
3. use / ought / you / sun cream / to
   _____
4. work / have / dad / all / summer / does / to / your / ?
   _____
5. guidebook / should / a / buy / we / ?
   _____
6. lie / you / for / too long / shouldn't / in the sun
   _____
7. to / do / I / have / mosquito / bring / spray / ?
   _____
8. forget / to / you / mustn't / your / take / passport
   _____

2 ● Match the sentence halves.
1. [c] If you're tired, you
2. [ ] My sister's eighteen now, so she
3. [ ] We can go to the airport by train, so we
4. [ ] Your cousins live in Paris, so you
5. [ ] Weigh your suitcase – it

a mustn't weigh more than fifteen kilos.
b ought to visit them while you're there.
c ~~should have some rest.~~
d has to pay the full price for tickets.
e don't have to drive there.

3 ●● Complete the sentences with the verb forms below. There are three extra forms you do not need.

don't have to pay	must go	must spend	mustn't pay
~~mustn't worry~~	should drink	shouldn't ask
shouldn't spend	will have to ask

1. You <u>mustn't worry</u> about anything – everything will be fine!
2. We've already paid for the hotel, so we _____ for anything when we get there.
3. Madrid is a beautiful city – you really _____ there.
4. You _____ plenty of water when you're out in the sun all day.
5. I know I _____ so much money on holiday, but I just love shopping!
6. I'd love to go on a camping trip with you, but I _____ my parents first.

4 ●● Complete the second sentence with the word in capitals so that it means the same as the first one. Use between two and five words.
1. I advise you to look online for the best deals.
   You <u>should look online</u> for the best deals. **SHOULD**
2. It isn't necessary to buy tickets in advance.
   You _____ tickets in advance. **HAVE**
3. You aren't allowed to play loud music in the hotel.
   You _____ loud music in the hotel. **MUST**
4. It will be necessary for us to get a bus to the hotel.
   We _____ a bus to the hotel. **HAVE**
5. It's a good idea to wear a sun hat when it's very hot.
   You _____ a sun hat when it's very hot. **OUGHT**

5 ●●● Complete the text with one modal verb in each gap. Do not use the same modal verb more than once.

Top tips for backpackers

First, you [1] <u>must</u> make sure you have all the documents you need before you set off – that's really important. You [2] _____ take sun cream if you are going somewhere hot. You [3] _____ have to phone your parents every day, but you [4] _____ to phone or email at least once a week, otherwise they'll get worried. You [5] _____ forget the date and time of your flight home. If you miss your flight, you [6] _____ pay for another one, and it will probably be expensive!

6.3 Reading and Vocabulary
Getting around Amsterdam

1 Complete the sentences with the words below.

| ~~bus stop~~ | pedestrians | route | return | single |
| traffic jam | travel card |

1 Where is the nearest *bus stop*, please? We want to go to the city centre.
2 There were so many cars in the _____ that we decided to park the car and walk.
3 My favourite bus _____ goes past the old part of the city. It's a good way to go sightseeing!
4 Do you want a _____ ticket for €3 or a _____ ticket for €5?
5 Students pay half price for a _____ and can use it for a month.
6 I want to live in a city that is safe for _____.

2 Read the text quickly. Tick (✓) the forms of transport that are mentioned.

1 ☐ bike   6 ☐ metro
2 ☐ boat   7 ☐ motorbike
3 ☐ bus   8 ☐ plane
4 ☐ car   9 ☐ train
5 ☐ cruise ship 10 ☐ tram

3 Read the text again. Answer the questions.

1 Where can you get a travel card in Amsterdam?
_____
2 What is one disadvantage of renting an electric boat?
_____
3 How can people avoid the traffic jams in Amsterdam?
_____

Getting around Amsterdam

Amsterdam is famous for its canals, museums and galleries. But what's the best way to travel around?

There's no need to choose just one type of transport in Amsterdam. The OV-chipkaart is a travel card which can be used on trams, buses and metros. You can buy it at tram or bus stops. You can also get a single ticket from the driver on a bus or tram if you only need to take one or two short journeys.

Amsterdam is sometimes called the 'Venice of the North'. It has around 165 canals, and the best way to explore them is by boat. There are different kinds of boats. Water buses go to all the popular attractions. If you want to go somewhere which isn't on the water bus route, there are water taxis which go everywhere. You can also rent electric boats. You can book online and you don't need a licence, but it's quite expensive. One hour costs around €60!

Or you can take a sightseeing cruise to see Amsterdam from the water.

You won't see many cars in Amsterdam. A lot of roads are only open for pedestrians and car parks are very expensive. The streets are also very narrow so there isn't much space to drive.

One way to avoid the traffic jams and have fun is to cycle. Thirty-eight percent of all journeys in the city are by bike because it is both safe and easy: there are 515 kilometres of cycle lanes and plenty of places to rent bikes for an hour, a day or even for the week. Prices start from €10 per day. If you decide to cycle, make sure you know the rules; for example at night you must have lights on your bike. You should also check what hand signals to use and where you can cycle. You might notice that many people who live in Amsterdam don't wear helmets, but we strongly recommend that you do.

I can understand an article about traffic and transport.

6.4 Grammar
Modal verbs: *must, could, may/might, can't* (speculation)

GRAMMAR — Modal verbs: *must, could, may/might, can't*

Speculation
It **must** be cold outside. People are in jackets.
It **may/might/could** be difficult to travel with the suitcase because it's very big.
That **can't** be our tent. It's the wrong colour.

1 ● Complete the sentences with *must* or *can't*.
1. That tent's tiny! It *can't* be big enough for eight people!
2. Look, that _____ be our hotel over there – I recognise it from the website.
3. The boat trips are very popular, so they _____ be good!
4. Everyone's swimming in the sea, so the water _____ be too cold.
5. The food in that restaurant looks amazing, so it _____ be expensive!
6. That _____ be our bus – our bus isn't due until 10.30, and it's only ten o'clock.

2 ● Choose the correct conclusion for each sentence.
1. Tom's gone home early.
   a) He might be ill.
   b He can't be ill.
2. I'm not sure where my phone is.
   a It must be in my bag.
   b It may be in my bag.
3. Carrie's shoes are black, but these ones are brown.
   a These could be Carrie's shoes.
   b These can't be Carrie's shoes.
4. I don't know where the museum is.
   a It might be near the station.
   b It can't be near the station.
5. Everyone's wearing T-shirts.
   a It must be hot.
   b It can't be hot.
6. I don't know what the museum's like. The guidebook doesn't mention it.
   a It might be interesting.
   b It must be interesting.

3 ●● Choose the correct answer.
1. Look, that boy's standing up in the pool – it ____ be very deep.
   a may   b) can't   c must
2. I guess this ____ be Jack's umbrella, but I'm really not sure.
   a must   b can't   c could
3. There are hundreds of people on the beach. It ____ be a very popular beach!
   a must   b might   c can't
4. I'm not sure if the gym is open now – it ____ be closed.
   a can't   b may   c must
5. Camping ____ be fun in the rain – I guess everything gets really wet!
   a must   b can't   c could
6. I don't know where he's from. I guess he ____ be French. Or maybe Spanish.
   a might   b must   c can't

4 ●●● Complete the dialogue. Choose the correct option.
A: Have you seen this website about an activity camp?
B: Yeah, it looks good. It ¹(might be)/ can't be fun to go on a holiday like this next summer. What do you think?
A: I agree. Do you think it costs a lot?
B: No, it ² must be / can't be expensive because it's for young people and they don't have much money.
A: That's true. What activities can you do?
B: Well, there's climbing. I don't know if I want to do that. I think it ³ can't be / must be scary being up so high.
A: Yes, you ⁴ may be / can't be right about that, but the other activities look really good fun.
B: Yeah, I love kayaking. Do you think Abbie ⁵ must be / might be interested in coming too? Should we ask her?
A: That's a good idea. I think it's definitely better to go with friends. It ⁶ could be / can't be lonely if you go on your own and you don't know anyone.

I can speculate about the present.

On the Portal
Extra Practice Activities: Lesson 6.4

6.5 Listening and Vocabulary
Millie lives the dream!

1 Choose the correct answer.
1. I think it's a good idea to ____ while you're still young.
   a trip b journey c travel
2. The hotel organises ____ to interesting tourist places.
   a excursions b travels c journeys
3. I enjoyed the day out, but the ____ back home took four hours!
   a travel b journey c excursion
4. We're planning a three-day ____ to New York next summer.
   a travel b trip c journey
5. Would you like to work in the ____ industry?
   a trip b voyage c travel
6. We were all tired after the long sea ____.
   a voyage b travel c journey

2 🔊 6.1 Listen to the first part of an interview. Which sentence is NOT true?
a Millie always goes on working holidays.
b Millie has visited nine different countries.
c Millie likes beach holidays.

3 🔊 6.2 Listen to the second part of the interview. Mark the sentences T (true) or F (false).
1. ☐ Millie first found out about Woofing online.
2. ☐ Millie always goes travelling when her job ends.
3. ☐ Millie enjoys working at summer camps the most.
4. ☐ You can work at activity camps even if you aren't good at sports.
5. ☐ You have to pay for food at activity camps.
6. ☐ Millie thinks that working holidays might be difficult for older people.

4 🔊 6.3 Listen and complete Millie's story with one or two words in each gap.

Last ¹*winter* I was in ² _____ teaching a group of teenagers how to ski. Most of them were already quite good, but one boy was a complete beginner. He was very good at ³ _____ and quickly learned how to turn and ⁴ _____. By the end of the week he was the ⁵ _____ in the group. On the last day he told me a story. ⁶ _____ before he was in a serious car accident. He lost part of his ⁷ _____ and used a prosthesis to walk. I had no idea he had a disability. I think that boy was amazing!

5 Match 1–6 with a–f to make compound nouns.
1. [c] organic   a trip
2. ☐ working   b desk
3. ☐ weekend   c ~~farm~~
4. ☐ ski   d money
5. ☐ reception   e holiday
6. ☐ pocket   f season

6 Write the correct compound noun for each definition. Use the nouns in Exercise 5.
1. a farm that grows food without using chemicals *organic farm*
2. a small amount of money you receive each week _____
3. a holiday where you do paid work _____
4. the place in a hotel where you check in when you arrive _____
5. a visit to a place on Saturday and Sunday _____
6. the period of time during the winter when there is enough snow to ski _____

I can understand a radio interview about travelling.

On the Portal
Extra Practice Activities: Lesson 6.5

6.6 Speaking
Understanding a conversation

1 🔊 **6.4** Listen and repeat the phrases.

> **SPEAKING** **Understanding a conversation**
>
> **Asking for clarification**
> Sorry, I didn't catch that.   What was that?
> Can you say that again?
> Sorry, I didn't get the first/last part.
> Could you speak more loudly/more slowly?
>
> **Clarifying**
> What I said was we are going on holiday.
> What I asked was what happened.
> I said (that) you have to take the Piccadilly line.
> I was just saying you can take the underground.
> I just wanted to ask (you) if you know that place.
> I just wanted to ask (you) about that place.

2 Match the sentence halves.
1. [d] Could you speak
2. [ ] Sorry, I didn't
3. [ ] I was just
4. [ ] I just wanted to
5. [ ] Can you
6. [ ] What I said

a saying that Jo isn't usually late.
b was that it sounds like a great idea.
c ask you about the Maths homework.
d ~~more slowly?~~
e catch that.
f say that again?

3 Order the sentences to make dialogues.
1. a [ ] What was that?
   b [ ] I was just saying, there's a good film on at the cinema tonight.
   c [1] Hey, Matt, there's a good film on at the cinema tonight.
2. a [ ] I said that Sam's busy, so he can't come to the party.
   b [ ] Maria can come to the party, but Sam's busy.
   c [ ] Sorry, I didn't get the last part.
3. a [ ] I just wanted to ask you about Friday.
   b [ ] Can you say that again?
   c [ ] Hi, Lily. What time are we meeting on Friday?

4 Complete the dialogues with sentences a–d.
1. A: Don't forget to pack your passport.
   B: Sorry, _b_.
   A: I said, don't forget to pack your passport.
2. A: Take the bus to the city centre. Then get on tram number 4.
   B: Sorry, ___.
   A: I said, take tram number 4.
3. A: I'll meet you at the station in ten minutes.
   B: What was that?
   A: ___, let's meet at the station in ten minutes.
4. A: Can you bring your guidebook with you?
   B: Could you speak more loudly, please?
   A: ___ you can bring your guidebook.
   B: Yes, of course.

a What I said was
b ~~I didn't catch that~~
c I was just asking if
d I didn't get the last part

5 🔊 **6.5** Complete the dialogues with one word in each gap. Listen and check.
1. Jo: Hi, Tom. Are you going on the school trip in November?
   Tom: Sorry, I didn't _catch_ that. It's very loud here. _____ you speak more loudly, please?
   Jo: I just _____ to ask you about the school trip in November.
   Tom: Oh. Yeah, I'm definitely going!
2. Sam: We need to be at the airport at ten.
   Jen: _____ was that?
   Sam: I _____ that we need to be at the airport at ten.
   Jen: OK.
3. Cara: Remember to pack your wetsuit because we might go diving if the sea's nice and clear.
   Mike: Sorry, could you _____ that again?
   Cara: _____ I said was that you should pack your wetsuit. We might go diving.
   Mike: Oh yeah. Good idea!

Unit 6 64 I can clarify what I have said and ask for clarification.

On the Portal
Extra Practice Activities: Lesson 6.6

6.7 Writing
An email about travel arrangements

1 Read the email and answer the questions.
1. What time does the plane leave?
2. Where will they sleep on the first night?
3. How will they travel to Krakow?

Hey Sammy,

① I just wanted to let you know about the plan.

② The plane leaves at 10 a.m. My dad will drive us to the terminal. While we wait we can have breakfast, so you don't have to eat before you come. Don't forget your passport!

③ When we arrive in Warsaw, we'll be tired, so I think we should stop there overnight. I've found a great hostel where we can stay. I'll send you the link. Let me know what you think. The next day we can go sightseeing. Then we could catch a train to Krakow in the evening. I've asked my Polish friend to meet us at the station. As soon as she replies, I'll let you know.

④ Let's talk later.

⑤ Bye for now,
Lucy

---

2 Read the email again. Match paragraphs 1–5 with topics a–e below.
a ☐ Ending your email
b ☐ Explaining arrangements
c ☐ Saying why you are writing
d ☐ Before you finish
e ☐ Making suggestions about the route

3 Complete the sentences with the words below.

| could | know | later | ~~let~~ | now | overnight | will |

1. I just wanted to *let* you know about the plan.
2. My dad _____ drive us to the station.
3. I think we should stop in London _____.
4. Let me _____ what you think.
5. We _____ catch a bus to Paris.
6. Let's talk _____.
7. Bye for _____.

4 Match the sentence halves.
1. [d] Here's a quick note
2. ☐ We're meeting at the station
3. ☐ It might be better to
4. ☐ See
5. ☐ Speak

a at 6 p.m.
b you soon.
c soon.
d ~~to tell you about the plan.~~
e take the bus.

5 Choose the correct option.
1. I'll give you your ticket *after* / (when) you arrive.
2. I'll call you *until* / *as soon as* I get back from my holiday.
3. *When* / *After* I see Paul, I'll ask him about his trip to China.
4. We'll tell someone where we're going *until* / *before* we go walking in the mountains.
5. Don't worry, we won't leave for the airport *until* / *as soon as* you get here.
6. We can go away *after* / *until* I finish all my exams.
7. I'll let you know *when* / *until* I find my passport.

WRITING TIME

6 You are going on a backpacking trip with a friend. Write an email about the travel arrangements.

1 Find ideas
Make notes about:
- the time and place to meet.
- what to take with you.
- the route to take.

2 Plan and write
- Organise your ideas into paragraphs. Use Lucy's email to help you.
- Write a draft email.

3 Check
- Check language: did you use future time clauses correctly?
- Check grammar: did you use modal verbs correctly?
- Write the final version of your email.

I can write an email about travel arrangements.

My Language File

WORDLIST 🔊 6.6

Types of holidays
- activity camp (n) _____
- backpacking holiday (n) _____
- beach holiday (n) _____
- camping trip (n) _____
- city break (n) _____
- ocean cruise (n) _____
- sightseeing holiday (n) _____

Word friends (going on holiday)
- book a hotel _____
- eat in/out (v) _____
- get on/off a bus _____
- get on/off a coach _____
- get on/off a plane _____
- get on/off a train _____
- go abroad _____
- go/travel around Europe _____
- go/travel around the world _____
- go/travel by boat/sea _____
- go/travel by car/road _____
- go/travel by plane/air _____
- go/travel by train/rail _____
- go on a cruise _____
- have a city break _____
- rent a holiday flat _____
- rent a bicycle _____
- rent a car _____
- stay on a campsite _____
- stay in a hostel _____

Holiday equipment
- guidebook (n) _____
- map (n) _____
- passport (n) _____
- rucksack/backpack (n) _____
- sleeping bag (n) _____
- suitcase (n) _____
- sun cream (n) _____
- sunglasses (n) _____
- swimsuit (n) _____
- tent (n) _____
- torch (n) _____

Holiday accommodation
- check in/out (v) _____
- double room (n) _____
- facilities (n) _____
- floor (n) _____
- guest (n) _____
- pool (n) _____
- reception (n) _____
- reservation (n) _____
- single room (n) _____
- view (n) _____

Traffic and transport
- pedestrian (n) _____
- return ticket (n) _____
- route (n) _____
- single ticket (n) _____
- traffic jam (n) _____
- travel card (n) _____

Travel: confusing words
- excursion (n) _____
- journey (n) _____
- travel (v, n) _____
- trip (n) _____
- voyage (n) _____

Extra words
- abroad (adv) _____
- airport (n) _____
- banned (adj) _____
- bridge (n) _____
- brilliant (adj) _____
- bring (v) _____
- campsite (n) _____
- canal (n) _____
- complain (v) _____
- convenient (adj) _____
- country (n) _____
- dark (adj) _____
- dirty (adj) _____
- get stuck _____
- gondola (n) _____
- island (n) _____
- jet ski (n) _____
- lovely (adj) _____
- Mediterranean (n) _____
- mosquito spray (n) _____
- narrow (adj) _____
- on board _____
- on foot _____
- permission (n) _____
- provide (v) _____
- rail trip (n) _____
- reserve (v) _____
- resident (n) _____
- ride (n) _____
- rowing boat (n) _____
- sailing holiday (n) _____
- station (n) _____
- stay (n) _____
- suitable (adj) _____
- super-friendly (adj) _____
- take turns _____
- tour (n) _____
- travel agent (n) _____
- youth hostel (n) _____

Sounds good!
- I can't hear a thing. _____
- You made it! _____
- Never mind. _____

MY LANGUAGE NOTES

My favourite words/expressions from this unit

Self-check

Vocabulary

1 Choose the correct option.
1. I'll make a hotel *reservation / reception* online.
2. There's a beautiful *floor / view* from my window.
3. We're planning to stay on a *campsite / camping*.
4. We went on a three-week *sightseeing / cruise* and really loved being on the ship.
5. There are two of us, so we need a *guest / double* room, please.
6. You can do lots of different sports at the activity *camp / trip*.
7. I wear *sun cream / sunglasses* to protect my eyes from the bright sun.
8. A *torch / map* will help you see in the dark.
9. Let's *plan / rent* a holiday flat.
10. I'm not interested in extra *facilities / guests* because I don't spend much time at the hotel.

2 Complete the sentences with the words below.

> return ticket   route   single ticket
> traffic jams   travel card

1. Can I buy a _____ to use all weekend?
2. Can I have a _____, please? I'm coming back this evening.
3. There are too many _____ in my hometown.
4. I need a _____ for just one journey.
5. Which bus _____ goes past the museum?

3 Order the letters to make words and complete the sentences.
1. I'm planning a short t_____ (PRIT) abroad.
2. I'd hate to go on a sea v_____ (GEYOVA).
3. Lea loves long train j_____ (RUNJEYOS).
4. Where is he going to t_____ (TAREVL) next?
5. Let's go on the cave e_____ (CSNEUXORI).

Grammar

4 Match sentences 1–7 with conclusions a–g.
1. ☐ I'm not sure whose coat this is.
2. ☐ Tina's already gone to bed!
3. ☐ I don't know when Max comes back.
4. ☐ You've just had a very big lunch.
5. ☐ I don't know where my passport is.
6. ☐ No one's in the sea today.
7. ☐ Alex is wearing shorts.

a It can't be very cold.
b It could be tomorrow.
c You can't be hungry!
d It may be in my bedroom.
e It might be John's.
f It must be too cold.
g She must be tired.

5 Decide if the sentences in each pair have the same meaning (S) or a different meaning (D).
1. ☐ a It's necessary for me to study.
       b I have to study.
2. ☐ a I advise you to be more careful.
       b You should be more careful.
3. ☐ a There is no need to pay.
       b You mustn't pay.
4. ☐ a It isn't a good idea to swim here.
       b You ought to swim here.
5. ☐ a They aren't allowed to go alone.
       b They mustn't go alone.
6. ☐ a It isn't necessary for you to meet me.
       b You don't have to meet me.
7. ☐ a They must drive slowly.
       b It's not necessary to drive slowly.
8. ☐ a You mustn't wear shoes inside.
       b You don't have to wear shoes inside.

Speaking

6 Complete the dialogues with the phrases below.

> didn't catch   first part   I said that
> say that again   what I asked

1. A: Are you ready?
   B: Sorry, I _____ that.
   A: _____ was if you're ready.
2. A: The train's late.
   B: Sorry, I didn't get the _____.
   A: _____ the train's late.
3. A: There's a special offer on cruises.
   B: Sorry, can you _____?

YOUR SCORE

Vocabulary: __/20   Speaking: __/5
Grammar: __/15   Total: __/40

Reading Time 2

The Railway Children

Roberta, Peter and Phyllis live happily in London with their parents. Then suddenly their father goes away. The children and their mother move to a smaller house near a railway line. Exciting things happen, and they make new friends. But where is their father? When is he coming home?

When the children came to live in their new home, they talked about their father all the time, but later they did not talk about him as much. Roberta thought that Mother was sad when they said his name.

'Is Father coming home one day?' she asked her mother.

'Yes, he is, but not for a long time.'

Roberta knew that her father was not ill or dead, but she did not understand why he was not with them. Mother told them nothing. All she said was, 'One day he's going to come home and then we can all be happy together again.'

The doctor looked at Peter's foot.

'He's going to be OK, but he must stay in bed.'

Peter did not like staying in bed because he had nothing to do. Roberta went to the station and asked Perks for any old newspapers for Peter to read.

'Yes, girl, I have a lot of old newspapers,' Perks said. 'Take these.'

Roberta carried them home, and she looked at them. Suddenly, she stopped and she read one newspaper story very carefully. When she finished, her face was white and sad. There was the name of her father. 'Five years in prison,' the newspaper said. 'This man is a spy!' Now she knew why Father did not come home. He was in prison!

'They are wrong,' she thought. 'My father isn't a bad man.'

Later she went to see her mother and showed her the newspaper.

'Oh, Roberta,' her mother said. 'Your father did not do anything wrong. Those two visitors in London were policemen. They thought Father was a spy after they found some letters. They took Father away.'

'But who was the spy?' Roberta asked.

'I don't know,' her mother said, 'but there was one man at your father's work – he didn't like Father. I think it was him.'

'What can we do?'

'We can only wait for Father to come home again.'

A week later Roberta wrote a letter. It was to the old man, their friend on the train. She cut the story out of the newspaper and sent it with her letter.

To my friend,

You see what it says in the newspaper about our father. But I know Father is not a spy. Someone put those papers and letters in Father's desk. Please help us to find the spy. Please, please help us.

Your friend, Roberta.

That afternoon she took the letter to the station. She gave it to the Station Master and asked him to give it to the old man the next day.

Before you read

1 Match sentences 1–4 with pictures A–D.
1. They robbed a bank to steal a lot of money, but they ended up in prison.
2. John le Carré was famous for writing stories about the famous spy, George Smiley.
3. When you're sick, you should stay in bed to get well.
4. I'd like to be a station master: this person knows everything about trains running at their station, operates the signals and makes sure that everything is safe.

A ☐
B ☐
C ☐
D ☐

2 Look at the book cover and read the blurb. What do you think happens in the story?

While you read

3 🔊 RT2.1 Read and listen to the story. Complete the sentences about the story with one word.
1. Talking about Father made Mother feel _____.
2. The doctor visited because Peter had a problem with his _____.
3. Roberta got some old _____ for Peter to read.
4. She read about her _____ in a newspaper.
5. The newspaper article said that Roberta's father was a _____.
6. Father went to _____ after the police found some letters.
7. Roberta contacted their _____ and asked him to help their father.
8. Their friend was an old man who they met on the _____.

4 Choose the correct answer.
1. Who is not a main character?
   a Roberta   b Roberta's father
   c Perks
2. What word does the author use at the beginning of a sentence to make the story exciting?
   a When   b Suddenly
   c Later
3. Which tense does the author mostly use to tell this story?
   a Past Simple   b Present Simple
   c Present Perfect

After you read

5 What do you think happens next in the story?

6 Read the summary and check your answers to Exercise 5.

Later, Peter gets better and the children go to watch some other children play a game. During the game, one of the boys goes into a tunnel, but doesn't come out. The children go after him and rescue the boy. They take him to their house and call the boy's grandfather. To their surprise, his grandfather is the old man on the train that Roberta wrote to. He promises to try and help their father. Some time later, the children are on the station platform when the train stops and a man gets off. It's their father! The old man kept his promise! They go home together and everyone is happy again.

7 **WRAP UP** Complete the information about the story.

Title: _____
Type: *love story / horror story / adventure story*
Main characters: _____
_____
Important object: _____
My opinion: ☆☆☆☆☆

69 Unit 6

People power

VOCABULARY Word building: family | Phrasal verbs | Collocations: relationships | Relations | Collocations with *get*

GRAMMAR Second Conditional | Relative clauses

7.1 Vocabulary
Family and friends

1 ● Match words 1–6 with definitions a–f.
1. [b] stepsister
2. [ ] great-grandmother
3. [ ] half-sister
4. [ ] stepbrother
5. [ ] stepmother
6. [ ] stepson

a a woman who is married to your father, who is not your mother
b ~~the daughter of your father's new wife~~
c a girl who shares only one parent with you
d a child that your husband or wife has from an earlier relationship or marriage
e the son of your stepfather or stepmother
f the mother of your grandmother

2 ●● Read the comments and write the family words.

> Tom's the same age as me. His mum is not my real mum, but she's married to my dad now. He's my ¹*stepbrother*.

> Elsie and Joe are my dad's grandparents, so they're my ² _____. Joe's nearly one hundred years old!

> Lucy's the youngest in my family and she's my ³ _____. We have the same mum, but we have different dads.

> My mum died when I was quite young. My dad's got a new wife now, Sara. I really like her, and I call her Mum, even though she isn't my real mother. She's my ⁴ _____.

> My aunt didn't have any children when she married a man with two daughters. She's now got two ⁵ _____.

3 ● Choose the correct option.
1. I *go* / *get* on really well with my cousin Jack – he's great!
2. You should talk to someone if you have a problem – don't just *deal* / *get* with it yourself.
3. I really enjoy *hanging* / *moving* out with my friends.
4. If you're feeling sad, you should go out *with* / *together* your friends and have some fun.
5. The whole family *got* / *went* together at the beach party last year.
6. I shared a bedroom with my sister when we were growing *up* / *away*.
7. I was really sad when my best friend moved *away* / *along* to a new town.

4 ●● Complete the sentences with the correct form of the phrasal verbs below.

| deal with | ~~get along with~~ | get on | get together |
| go out | grow up | hang out with | move away |

1. I don't *get along with* my sister at all – we're completely different and she just annoys me.
2. He has a lot of problems to _____, so he's quite stressed.
3. When I moved to a new school, I _____ a lot because I wanted to make new friends.
4. My sister _____ to London when she started university.
5. Do you want to _____ to work on the project? You can come to my house on Saturday.
6. I prefer to _____ just a small group of friends. I don't like big crowds.
7. When you _____ in the countryside, you can play outside much more.
8. Do you _____ well with everybody in your class?

5 ● **WORD FRIENDS** Look at the pictures. Choose the correct answer.

1   a   She sees her friends after school.
    b   She likes spending time with her brother.
    c   They often have an argument.

2   a   They don't share any interests.
    b   They aren't getting to know each other.
    c   They have the same sense of humour.

3   a   They are having an argument.
    b   They're getting to know each other.
    c   They have a lot in common.

6 ●● Complete the sentences with the words below. There are two extra words.

argument   ~~get~~   have   make   own
see   sense   share   time

1   I'm quite a shy person – it takes me a while to *get* to know people.
2   I love spending _____ with my sister.
3   Aya and I _____ an interest in climbing, so we have lots to talk about.
4   Jo and Beth have an _____ at least once a week. I don't know why they are friends.
5   My friends and I usually _____ each other after school.
6   I think it's important for friends to have the same _____ of humour.
7   My brothers and I _____ something in common – we all love football!

I can talk about relationships with my family and friends.

7 ●●● Complete the text with one word in each gap.

Your problems Emma's here to help!

My mum and dad got divorced two years ago and my dad has just got married again. I really don't ¹*get* on with his wife, my new ² _____. She's got two daughters already, so I've now got two ³ _____. I know I should be happy for my dad, but she doesn't want to ⁴ _____ any time with me. What's worse, I don't ⁵ _____ any interests with her kids! I just stay in my bedroom all the time now because I don't know how to ⁶ _____ with this situation. Help!

Emma says:
It can be difficult when a parent gets a new partner, especially when there are also new children to add to your family. It will take time for you to ⁷ _____ to know your dad's new wife, so just be patient. But hopefully, if you make the effort and hang ⁸ _____ with the whole family, you will discover that things improve.

Have your say! 2 comments

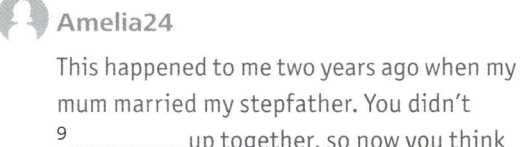

Amelia24
This happened to me two years ago when my mum married my stepfather. You didn't ⁹ _____ up together, so now you think you have nothing in common. But try to talk to them more. Who knows, maybe you ¹⁰ _____ the same sense of humour?

SaraG
Don't spend too much time at home if you find it stressful. You need to ¹¹ _____ together with friends when you can. The others are right – it takes time, but I'm sure that if you make the effort with your new family members, in time you will all get along ¹² _____ each other fine.

On the Portal
Extra Practice Activities: Lesson 7.1

7.2 Grammar
Second Conditional

> **GRAMMAR** — **Second Conditional**
> **If** her flight **arrived** earlier, **I'd be** able to go to the airport.
> What **would** you **do** if you **were** me?

1 ● Match the sentence halves.
1. [d] Max would do better in exams
2. [ ] If I didn't have any friends,
3. [ ] You wouldn't be so tired
4. [ ] If you had the chance to go travelling,
5. [ ] Would you be pleased
6. [ ] If I were you,

a I'd be really lonely.
b if your friends organised a party for you?
c I'd go to the end-of-term party on Friday.
d ~~if he worked harder.~~
e if you went to bed earlier.
f which countries would you visit?

2 ● Choose the correct option.
1. I *will be* / *(would be)* really happy if my dad would *get* / *(got)* married again
2. What *would* / *will* you do if your best friend *was* / *would be* upset with you?
3. If I *had* / *would have* plenty of money, I *will take* / *would take* all my friends out for a meal.
4. If I *were* / *would be* you, I *don't worry* / *wouldn't worry* about what other people think.

3 ●● Complete the second sentence so that it means the same as the first one. Use the Second Conditional.
1. I have a lot of exams this year, so I'm really stressed.
   I *wouldn't be* so stressed if I *didn't have* a lot of exams.
2. Jack's parents always get worried when he gets bad grades at school.
   Jack's parents _____ worried if he _____ better grades at school.
3. I'm not old enough to watch that film.
   I _____ that film if I _____ older.
4. I don't have a big house, so I won't invite many people to the party.
   I _____ more people to the party if I _____ a bigger house.

4 ●● Complete the text messages with the correct form of the verbs below. Use the Second Conditional.

be (x2)   know   not remember   not worry

> Hi, Jenna! Help! I need some advice. It's Abi's birthday next Saturday, but I don't have much money. What can I give her?

> If I ¹*were* you, I ² _____ about buying expensive gifts. That's not what friendship is about. Sure, Abi ³ _____ upset if you ⁴ _____ her birthday, but I'm sure she'd feel bad if she ⁵ _____ you were so worried. Just relax! Buy her some flowers and give her a big birthday hug!

5 ●●● Complete the article with one word in each gap.

Money or friends?

What ¹*would* you do if you won £10 million? ² _____ you had that amount of money, you ³ _____ need to work – ever! Just imagine that! If you ⁴ _____ have to work, you ⁵ _____ be able to spend your life travelling or relaxing — doing exactly what you wanted. Does that sound good to you?

Most people imagine that if they ⁶ _____ rich, they would ⁷ _____ happier. They think that if money ⁸ _____ not a problem for them, they ⁹ _____ have any worries in the world. But in reality, it seems this isn't true. Psychologists have found that what really makes us happy is our family and friends, and money can't buy those.

I can use the Second Conditional to talk about unreal or imaginary situations.

On the Portal
Extra Practice Activities: Lesson 7.2

7.3 Reading and Vocabulary
Making friends

1 Complete the words in the sentences.
1 Your m _a_ t _e_ s are your friends.
2 Your c_____ m_____ s are the people you have lessons with at school.
3 Your b___ t f_____ s are the ones you like the most.
4 Someone you don't know is a s_____ g__ r.
5 People that you play football, hockey or other sports with are your t___ mm___ s.

2 Complete the sentences with the correct form of the words below.

| be | have | keep | ~~make~~ |

1 Some people don't find it easy to _make_ new friends.
2 Everyone needs to _____ friends that they can talk to when they have problems.
3 Sam's a very popular guy – he _____ friends with everyone in the class!
4 It can be hard to _____ your old friends when you move away to a new town.

3 Read the article quickly and match paragraphs 1–5 with topics a–e below.
a ☐ The Coach
b ☐ The Classmate
c ☐ The Honest One
d ☐ The Supporter
e ☐ The Adventurer

4 Read the article again and complete the sentences with no more than three words in each gap.
1 The article tells us about _____ everyone should have.
2 Friends who support you will _____ with you any time.
3 When a friend always tells you the truth, you might sometimes think they aren't _____.
4 You won't have a problem getting to know a classmate because you'll have _____.
5 When you enjoy your routine, it can be difficult to try _____.
6 Friends don't have to be _____ you to teach you something.
7 The writer of the article wants you to _____.

I can understand an article about friendship.

FRIENDS WE ALL NEED

Best friends are important, but research shows that we need a variety of different friends to be happy. Here are the five friends you really need.

1 This friend is your biggest fan. They always have time to hang out with you and really care about you. He or she is a good listener and loves to help you to deal with problems, even small ones. What's more, they will always support you no matter what, so you can always count on them.

2 This friend will always tell you the truth, even when it hurts. They don't want to listen to you complain about your family or your homework. They'll tell you to stop whining and deal with it. It is not that they are not interested. They feel this is the right way to help you. This friend will surely make you a better person, even if sometimes you think they're not on your side.

3 We don't always go to the same school as our best friends, but that doesn't mean you have to sit on your own. Make friends with your classmates. It will be easy because you already have something in common: your school. Do it and you'll have someone who understands your homework problems, and you'll definitely enjoy your lessons more.

4 It's not easy to try something new, especially when you love hanging out with your friends, watching a film and eating your favourite snacks. That's why this friend is so important. They are always ready to experience new activities, cultures and places. Routine is good, but remember: there is a big world out there to explore.

5 We can learn from teachers, parents and brothers and sisters. But we can also learn from our friends. This friend doesn't have to be older than you. They just need to be really good at something, have some skills, knowledge or experiences to share. Join a club or start a new hobby. You'll meet plenty of people to choose from.

So, how many of these friends do you have? Have we forgotten any other important friends? Let us know what you think.

On the Portal
Extra Practice Activities: Lesson 7.3

7.4 Grammar
Relative clauses

GRAMMAR — Relative clauses

Defining relative clauses (essential information)
Ben is a friend who/that always listens.
One thing which/that I'd rescue is my handheld console.
Our youth club is one place where I like to relax.

Non-defining relative clauses (extra information)
Mr Kipling, who was my first teacher, was the most helpful.
We Will Rock You, which is my dad's favourite, is in my head.
Iceland, where there are loads of volcanoes, is a place I'd love to visit.

1 ● Complete the sentences 1–5 with relative clauses a–e.
1 The house _e_ has got a big garden.
2 The men ____ both had dark hair.
3 The car ____ is quite old.
4 There's a small café on the beach ____.
5 Mrs Perks, ____, is a dance teacher.

a where they sell really nice ice cream.
b which my mum drives
c who lives in my street
d that I saw near the bank
e that my parents want to buy

2 ●● Combine the sentences using relative clauses. Use *who*, *which* or *where*. Add commas where necessary.
1 My cousin is very good at football. He's three years older than me.
   My cousin, _who is three years older than me, is_ very good at football.
2 Edinburgh is about 600 kilometres from London. It's the capital of Scotland.
   Edinburgh _____ about 600 kilometres from London.
3 Jo showed me the house. She lived there when she was younger.
   Jo showed me _____ when she was younger.
4 We met a man. He grows vegetables for the market.
   We met a man _____ for the market.
5 Bournemouth is on the coast. My grandparents live there.
   Bournemouth _____ on the coast.

3 ●● Choose the correct answer.

Real friends?

Do you think of all the people [1]____ you know online as your friends? It seems that a lot of the people [2]____ use social media sites, such as Facebook, have over 200 online friends, compared to around fifty 'real' friends, [3]____ they actually meet in real life. Facebook, [4]____ was started in 2004, now has around 2.9 billion users worldwide, and a lot of people see it as a place [5]____ they can meet new friends as well as keep in touch with old ones. Studies [6]____ have looked at how people behave on social media sites have found that people are sometimes more honest and open online than they are in real life. But psychologists say, it is our ten or twelve closest relationships [7]____ are the most important to us. So maybe it's still better to and meet your friends in the local park or café, [8]____ you can talk face to face.

	a	b	c
1	which	**(b) who**	where
2	that	where	what
3	which	that	who
4	what	which	who
5	where	that	which
6	that	who	where
7	who	where	which
8	which	where	that

4 ●●● Find and correct the mistakes in the sentences. Remember to check for commas.
1 That's the café which we sometimes have lunch.
   That's the café where we sometimes have lunch.
2 The prize what we won wasn't very exciting.
   _____
3 Sophie who is French can speak French and English.
   _____
4 Their car, that is over twenty years old, still works well.
   _____
5 I lent the book to Dan, which loves adventure stories.
   _____

Unit 7 — I can use defining and non-defining relative clauses to describe people, things and places.

On the Portal
Extra Practice Activities: Lesson 7.4

7.5 Listening and Vocabulary
A helpful friend

1 **WORD FRIENDS** What does *get* mean in each sentence? Choose the correct option.
1. We didn't **get** home until after midnight!
   become / (arrive) / leave
2. I **get** bored quite quickly if I have nothing to do.
   make / bring / become
3. I **got** an email from my uncle yesterday.
   received / arrived / wrote
4. I need to **get** a new pair of jeans.
   make / change / buy
5. My brother is trying to **get** a job.
   pay / find / leave
6. Shall I **get** you a hot drink?
   take / find / bring

2 🔊 **7.1** Listen to a teacher talking about a buddy system for students with autism in her school. Choose the correct answer.
1. What does the teacher say about autism?
   a It's a disability.
   b It isn't very common.
   c It can cause social problems for some students.
2. When are buddies most needed?
   a during lessons
   b at break time
   c before and after school
3. What is the best description of a buddy?
   a a helper
   b a best friend
   c a teacher
4. What has surprised the teachers?
   a The buddies have learned a lot from the experience.
   b There are now fewer students with autism.
   c Students with autism now have fewer problems in class.

3 🔊 **7.2** Listen to Joey talking about being a buddy. Choose the correct answer.
1. What do we learn about Joey and Matt?
   a They were friends before the buddy scheme started.
   b They are in the same class.
   c They share the same friends.
2. What did Matt find difficult?
   a chatting to people
   b spending time alone
   c joining in with activities
3. What did Joey help Matt to do?
   a become better at sport
   b have the confidence to make friends
   c deal with strangers
4. What has Joey learned from the experience?
   a Everyone can be a good buddy.
   b It isn't easy to make friends.
   c People with different hobbies can be interesting.

4 🔊 **7.2** Complete the sentences with the phrases below. Listen and check.

get a lot out of	get into	gets quite stressed
~~got back~~		

1. I first started being a buddy when I *got back* to school after the summer holidays.
2. He explained that he _____ if there are people around him.
3. If he gets a bit better, I think he'll _____ the school team!
4. I _____ the whole experience of being a buddy.

I can understand a conversation about helping people in need.

7.6 Speaking
Identifying people in a group

1 🔊 **7.3** Listen and repeat the phrases.

> **SPEAKING** — Identifying people in a group
>
> **Talking about people in a group**
> He's/She's standing/sitting/talking to/playing with them.
> He's/She's wearing blue jeans.
> He's/She's in front of/behind/next to/near the teacher.
> He's/She's on the left/on the right/in the middle.
> He's/She's at the front/at the back/in the foreground/in the background.
>
> **Asking**
> Who's this/that boy/girl on the left/who is wearing trainers?
> Which one/girl/boy/man/woman/guy?
> Which one do you mean?
>
> **Explaining**
> The one with/who is my friend.
> The tall/good-looking one.

2 Match the question halves.
1. [f] Who's the boy on
2. [ ] Who's the girl who is
3. [ ] Who's that guy next
4. [ ] Which one
5. [ ] Who's the woman at
6. [ ] Who's the young child in

a wearing a blue dress?
b do you mean?
c the front, by the door?
d the middle?
e to your grandmother?
f ~~the left?~~

3 Complete the sentences with the words below.

> back   near   one   playing   standing
> ~~talking~~   tall   wearing

1. That's Paul, there. He's _talking_ to my Uncle George.
2. Look, there's my Aunt Paula. She's at the _____, behind my cousin Freddie.
3. She's _____ a really nice dress.
4. Toby's on the left, _____ the window.
5. There's my half-brother Dave. He's _____ next to my brother Matty.
6. That's my little cousin Tilly. She's _____ with a ball. Look, she's really cute!
7. Mike's the _____ who is wearing a red tie.
8. Abigail's the _____ one, in the pink dress.

4 Order the sentences to make dialogues.
1. a [ ] Which one do you mean?
   b [ ] She's wearing a green hat.
   c [ ] Who's that girl in the foreground?
   d [ ] That's Clara. She's my stepsister.
2. a [ ] He is good-looking.
   b [ ] Hey Jake. Look at this photo from the party. Which one is your cousin?
   c [ ] He's in the front, talking to Maya.
   d [ ] Yeah, he's cool.
3. a [ ] Who's that guy in the photo?
   b [ ] The one on the right at the back.
   c [ ] That's Mark.
   d [ ] Which one?

5 🔊 **7.4** Complete the dialogue with the words below. There are two extra words. Listen and check.

> background   on   right   standing
> wearing   which   who's   ~~with~~

Liz: Hi, there. What are you two doing?
Kim: I'm just showing Mia the photos from my family party last month. Remember? It was my grandad's seventieth birthday. The girl ¹_with_ me is my cousin Beth.
Liz: Oh yeah. She looks nice.
Kim: She is. We get on really well.
Mia: ²_____ that boy?
Kim: ³_____ one?
Mia: The one in the ⁴_____, behind you. The one who's ⁵_____ a blue jumper.
Kim: Oh that's my half-brother. He was at my birthday party last year.
Liz: Oh yes! I remember. And who's that guy that's ⁶_____ next to your brother?
Kim: That's my friend Jack. He lives in Manchester.

Unit 7 — 76 — I can explain who I am talking about.

On the Portal
Extra Practice Activities: Lesson 7.6

7.7 Writing
A short story

1 Read Emma's story. Choose the correct answer.
1. What does Emma tell us to set the scene?
   a She wants to make some new friends.
   b She wants to celebrate the end of exams.
2. What is the first event in the story?
   a Emma talks to Gabby.
   b Emma invites Alfie.
3. What else happens in the story?
   a Gabby decides that the new girl is boring.
   b Emma decides to invite the new girl.
4. What is the climax of the story?
   a Vera gets on well with everyone.
   b Gabby is bored at the party.
5. What is the outcome of the story?
   a Emma wants to make more friends.
   b Emma and Vera are friends.

Making a new friend

① Last weekend I wanted to celebrate the end of exams. I decided to invite a few friends over to my house for pizza.

② First, I asked my best friend Gabby. 'Great idea,' she said.

③ Next, we planned who else to invite. 'If you don't invite Alfie, he'll be really upset,' Gabby said. I agreed, so I sent him a message.

④ Just then, I noticed the new girl in our class, who is very quiet. To be honest, I thought she was a bit boring. 'I think I'll invite the new girl,' I said to Gabby. Afterwards, I went and asked her. 'I'd love to come,' she said.

⑤ That weekend we had a great time. Everyone who came had fun, and you'll never guess what happened next. The new girl, Vera, wasn't boring at all. We have the same sense of humour and she made us all laugh a lot. Now we're good friends! In future I won't be so quick to judge people.

2 Read the story again. Match paragraphs 1–5 with topics a–e below.
a ☐ The first event
b ☐ Setting the scene
c ☐ The second event
d ☐ The outcome
e ☐ The main event or climax

3 Complete the sentences with the time words below.

> afterwards   ~~first~~   just   next

1. *First*, we wrote invitations.
2. _____, we planned what music to play.
3. _____ then, my best friend called.
4. _____, we watched a film.

4 Mark the sentences S (starting the story and setting the scene), C (climax) or E (ending).
1. You'll never guess what happened next. *C*
2. All's well that ends well. ___
3. Have you ever had a really terrible day? ___
4. I can't wait to do that again! ___
5. My first day of school was an awesome day. ___
6. Then I had a real surprise. ___

WRITING TIME

5 Write a story about organising an event and making a new friend.

1 Find ideas
Make notes about:
- what event you wanted to organise.
- what you talked about and planned.
- what you learned about friendship from your experience.

2 Plan and write
- Organise your ideas into paragraphs. Use Emma's story to help you.
- Write a draft story.

3 Check
- Check language: did you use sequencers correctly?
- Check grammar: did you mostly use the Past Simple and some conditional? Did you use relative clauses correctly?
- Write the final version of your story.

I can write a short story.

My Language File

WORDLIST 🔊 7.5

Word building (family)
great-grandfather (n) _____
great-grandmother (n) _____
great-grandparent (n) _____
half-brother (n) _____
half-sister (n) _____
stepbrother (n) _____
stepdaughter (n) _____
stepfather (n) _____
stepmother (n) _____
stepsister (n) _____
stepson (n) _____

Phrasal verbs
deal with (a problem) (v) _____
get along with (v) _____
get on with (v) _____
get together (v) _____
go out (with) (v) _____
grow up (v) _____
hang out with (v) _____
move away (v) _____

Word friends (relationships)
get to know someone _____
have an argument _____
have something in common _____
have the same sense of humour _____
see each other after school _____
share an interest in something _____
spend time with someone _____

Relations (people)
best friend (n) _____
classmate (n) _____
mate (n) _____

stranger (n) _____
teammate (n) _____

(phrases with friend(s))
be friends _____
have a friend _____
keep friends _____
make friends _____

Word friends (phrases with get)
get a hot drink (for someone) _____
get a job _____
get a letter/a phone call/an email _____
get a pet _____
get better/worse _____
get bored/excited/upset _____
get dressed _____
get home _____
get old(er) _____
get ready _____

Extra words
arrive (v) _____
aunt (n) _____
biological (adj) _____
character (n) _____
complicated (adj) _____
cousin (n) _____
dilemma (n) _____
disagree (v) _____
disappointed (adj) _____
end-of-term party (n) _____
family meal (n) _____
fetch (v) _____
flight (n) _____
friendly (adj) _____
friendship (n) _____

generation (n) _____
hand-held console (n) _____
home town (n) _____
invitation (n) _____
likes and dislikes _____
long-lost (adj) _____
loud (adj) _____
marriage (n) _____
miss somebody (v) _____
neighbour (n) _____
nightmare (n) _____
opinion (n) _____
parent (n) _____
positive (adj) _____
recognise (v) _____
related by blood _____
relation (n) _____
relative (n) _____
reply (v) _____
rescue (v) _____
researcher (n) _____
rewind (v) _____
shared (adj) _____
similar (adj) _____
social identity (n) _____
step (n) _____
tell the whole story _____
thought (n) _____
uncle (n) _____
volunteer (v) _____
wedding (n) _____

Sounds good!
What are you up to? _____
How romantic! _____

MY LANGUAGE NOTES

My favourite words/expressions from this unit

Unit 7 78

Self-check

Vocabulary

1 Choose the correct option.
1. Do you *go / hang* out for a meal every week?
2. When does your whole family *see / get* together?
3. My mum and her new husband are having a baby girl. She'll be my *half-sister / stepsister*.
4. Dan and I have the *common / same* sense of humour.
5. Paul and his sister often *get / have* an argument when they are stressed.
6. Sara and I have a lot in *common / together*.
7. Moira *gets / grows* along with both her brothers.
8. They enjoy *sharing / spending* time together.
9. I really enjoyed my father's wedding to my new *stepmother / stepdaughter*.

2 Complete the sentences with the words below.

> best friend   classmates   mate   strangers   teammates

1. I'm really bad at talking to _____, so I find it hard to make new friends.
2. Agata is my _____, we tell each other everything.
3. Jenny is a good _____, but I don't discuss my problems with her.
4. After the match I usually eat pizza with all my _____ to talk about the game together.
5. I don't usually see my _____ outside of school, but I get on with all of them.

3 Match the examples of *get* 1–6 in the text with the meanings a–f.

When I ¹**got** home from school, I ²**got** a phone call. It was my stepdad. He told me he ³**got** me a job at the local football stadium. I love football, so I started to ⁴**get** very excited. He told me I would be working in the restaurant, ⁵**getting** snacks for fans. I really want to ⁶**get** a bike, so I'm going to save up all the money I earn and soon I will buy one.

a   arrive ____
b   become ____
c   bring/fetch ____
d   buy ____
e   find ____
f   receive ____

Grammar

4 Complete the Second Conditional sentences with the correct form of the verbs in brackets.
1. If you _____ more time practising, you _____ better at playing the piano. (spend/get)
2. We _____ to the beach if it _____ sunny. (go/be)
3. If I _____ more money, I _____. (have/travel)
4. I _____ to someone about this problem if I _____ you. (talk/be)
5. She _____ more exercise if she _____ near a gym. (do/live)
6. If I _____ drawing, I _____ Art at university. (enjoy/study)
7. I _____ how to surf if I _____ more time. (learn/have)
8. If I _____ the answer, I _____ you. (know/help)

5 Choose the correct option.
1. He's the boy *who / which* sits next to me.
2. That's the park *that / where* we hang out.
3. My grandmother, *that / who* is seventy-six, is still very fit and active.
4. Is that the bike *who / that* you won?
5. Leeds, *when / which* is in the north of England, is a popular city for students.
6. She's the girl *where / who* comes from Spain.
7. There's a lake *where / that* you can hire boats.

Speaking

6 Complete the dialogue with the phrases below.

> one do   one with   that boy   the back   which one

A: Do you want to see the photos from the party?
B: Sure! Who's ¹_____ on the left?
A: Which ²_____ you mean?
B: The tall ³_____ dark hair.
A: That's Luke. And that's my cousin I told you about.
B: ⁴_____?
A: He's at ⁵_____ eating cake!

YOUR SCORE

Vocabulary: __/20   Speaking: __/5
Grammar: __/15   Total: __/40

Just justice

VOCABULARY
Crimes and criminals | Solving crimes | The law | Word building: negative adjectives | Investigating crimes

GRAMMAR
Present and Past Simple passive | have/get something done

8 8.1 Vocabulary
Crime

1 ● Complete the words in the sentences.
1. A t**h** **i** **e**f took a lot of expensive jewellery from my grandfather's shop.
2. There aren't many v___d__ls in my city, but someone broke this window last night.
3. I saw a p___kp_____t on the bus. She tried to take a man's wallet.
4. What would you do if you saw a sh___l___t__r put something in their bag without paying?
5. I'd be scared if I found a b__r_____r in my house.
6. I like watching movies about bank r__b___rs.

2 ● **WORD FRIENDS** Choose the correct option.
1. (steal) / solve things
2. solve / break into homes
3. solve / steal crimes
4. commit / rob a crime
5. rob / steal a bank
6. commit / damage buildings
7. damage / break the law

3 ●● Choose the correct answer.
1. The ____ tried to take my wallet, but he fell over and dropped it.
   a vandal   (b) pickpocket   c burglar
2. The film is about a woman who ____ a bank and never got caught!
   a stole   b broke   c robbed
3. She's famous for ____ very difficult crimes.
   a solving   b damaging   c stealing
4. He didn't know he was breaking the ____ when he crossed the road on a red light.
   a thief   b crime   c law
5. Last night some ____ destroyed the plants outside my house.
   a pickpockets   b vandals   c thieves
6. A burglar broke ____ my grandfather's house and took his computer.
   a to   b into   c up

4 ● Choose the correct option.
1. The police finally caught the (burglars) / burglaries.
2. We're lucky because there isn't much vandals / vandalism in this town.
3. The bank robbers / robberies got away with over £500,000.
4. Is it shoplifters / shoplifting if you try on a coat, but forget to pay when you leave the shop?
5. A pickpocket / pickpocketing stole my phone.
6. She is upset by the thief / theft of her car.

5 ● Match the sentence halves.
1. [d] She had to pay a £300
2. [ ] The bank has offered a
3. [ ] My mother works
4. [ ] He wasn't sent to
5. [ ] What would be a suitable
6. [ ] You will need a good
7. [ ] My uncle has to go to
8. [ ] What is the typical sentence

a reward of £10,000 for information about the crime.
b punishment for this crime?
c court tomorrow. He saw a burglary.
d ~~fine for shoplifting.~~
e lawyer to help you.
f prison because he was too young.
g as a judge. It's a difficult job.
h for shoplifting in your country?

6 ● Order the letters and complete the words in the sentences.

1. The burglar left one f*ingerprint* (RENINFIGPRT) on the window.
2. There are s_____ (RESICUTY) cameras all over the city.
3. They are going to interview the s_____ (CEPSUST) now.
4. It's a very difficult c_____ (SACE) to solve.
5. It takes a lot of training to become a d_____ (VITEDTECE).
6. How would you feel if you were a w_____ (SENWITS) to a serious crime?

7 ●● Complete the sentences with the words below. There is one extra word.

| court | fine | judge | lawyer | ~~prison~~ | punishment | reward |

1. Matt spent fifteen years in *prison* for his crimes.
2. Everyone in _____ was shocked by the details of this terrible crime.
3. He will receive a harsh _____ for this crime.
4. The _____ decides how long someone should spend in prison.
5. You often pay a _____ for crimes like driving faster than the speed limit allows.
6. Jen got a _____ of £50 for taking the missing bag to the police station.

8 ●●● Read the texts and choose the correct answer.

1. a robbing   (b) damaging   c stealing
2. a vandal   b burglary   c vandalism
3. a prison   b fine   c reward
4. a punishment b law   c court
5. a shoplifters b vandals   c thieves
6. a robbed   b broke   c stole
7. a lawyers   b robbers   c witnesses
8. a clues   b cases   c fingerprints
9. a punishment b fine   c reward
10. a shoplifter b vandal   c pickpocket
11. a commit   b solve   c damage
12. a judge   b court   c fine

I can talk about crime and criminals.

The Westbury Times

THEY NEED TO LEARN A LESSON!

Two teenagers were arrested for [1]____ their school building yesterday. The two boys broke windows in the building and sprayed paint over it. The police said [2]____ of this kind was very serious. The teenagers are too young to go to [3]____, but the police hope the [4]____ they receive will be serious enough to teach them a lesson.

INFORMATION NEEDED

The police are asking for help from the public after [5]____ got away with two valuable paintings. The criminals [6]____ into the town's art gallery last night. There were no [7]____, but the police hope the gallery's security cameras will give them some [8]____. The art gallery is offering a [9]____ of £10,000 for the safe return of the two paintings.

BRAVE GRANDMOTHER CATCHES A CRIMINAL

Sixty-two-year-old grandmother Beryl Bridges was shocked when she saw a [10]____ stealing someone's wallet near the station on Saturday. She chased after the man and caught him when he tripped and fell. 'It makes me really angry when people [11]____ crimes,' Beryl said. 'They shouldn't get away with it!' The man will appear in [12]____ tomorrow.

On the Portal
Extra Practice Activities: Lesson 8.1

8.2 Grammar
Present and Past Simple passive

GRAMMAR — The passive

Present Simple passive
The quote *is* never really *used* by Sherlock Holmes.
Past Simple passive
The detective stories *were written* by a British author.

1 Complete the table. Write the verb forms and mark the verbs R (regular) or I (irregular).

Verb	Past Simple	Past Participle	Regular/Irregular
ask	¹ asked	asked	R
build	built	²	
catch	³	caught	
chase	chased	⁴	
hide	⁵	hidden	
make	made	⁶	
see	⁷	seen	
use	used	⁸	
watch	⁹	watched	
write	wrote	¹⁰	

2 Choose the correct option.
1 The two robbers *was / (were)* caught as they were leaving the bank.
2 *Is / Are* a lot of science used to solve crimes nowadays?
3 *Was / Were* a secret microphone hidden under her clothes?
4 Sometimes ordinary people *is / are* asked to help the police with information.
5 Security cameras *isn't / aren't* used in the shopping centre.

3 Order the words to make sentences.
1 my / stolen / purse / pickpocket / was / a / by
   My purse was stolen by a pickpocket.
2 every year / a lot of / stolen / mobile phones / are
   _____
3 asked / she / questions / the police / by / was
   _____
4 some / reported / aren't / to / the police / crimes
   _____
5 your / car / when / stolen / was / ?
   _____

4 Complete the second sentence so that it means the same as the first one. Use no more than three words.
1 They hid the paintings in their van.
   The paintings *were hidden in* their van.
2 A shop assistant caught the shoplifter.
   The shoplifter _____ a shop assistant.
3 Millions of people watch crime dramas on TV.
   Crime dramas _____ millions of people on TV.
4 Did they send the thief to prison?
   Was _____ to prison?
5 People steal a lot of jewellery from this shop.
   A lot of jewellery _____ this shop.
6 They didn't find the missing money.
   The missing money _____.

5 Complete the article with the correct passive form of the verbs below.

~~create~~   help   know   make   publish   solve   watch

The Belgian detective

The character of the Belgian detective Hercule Poirot ¹ *was created* by the writer Agatha Christie in the 1920s. Between 1920 and 1975, over eighty Poirot novels and short stories ² _____. In the stories, Poirot sometimes works alone, but usually he ³ _____ by his assistant, Captain Hastings. Poirot always dresses smartly and he ⁴ _____ for his neat moustache and his polite manners. He is very intelligent and believes that all crimes ⁵ _____ by using the 'little grey cells' in your brain.

In 2017, a new version of a Poirot story, *Murder on the Orient Express*, ⁶ _____ by the famous director, Kenneth Branagh. But even today, Poirot films from the 1970s ⁷ _____ by millions of people each year on TV.

On the Portal
Extra Practice Activities: Lesson 8.2

8.3 Reading and Vocabulary
The right punishment?

1 Complete the sentences with the negative form of the adjectives below.

> important   interesting   legal   ~~logical~~   patient
> responsible   usual

1. Why do you wash your hands before having a shower? It's completely *illogical*.
2. If you do something _____, the police will come after you.
3. That's a very _____ plant – I've never seen one like it before.
4. It was very _____ to stay up so late the night before the exam.
5. The fingerprint was _____. It wasn't connected to the crime.
6. Henry hates waiting. He's really _____.
7. I didn't enjoy that lesson. It was really _____.

2 Read the article. Choose the correct answer.
1. Why did Roberta hack into her school's records?
   a. She wanted to make money by selling the information she found.
   b. Her schoolwork was boring and she needed some excitement.
   c. She always wanted to be a hacker.
   d. She wanted to see if she could do it.
2. Why didn't Roberta go to a court?
   a. Because she was still a teenager.
   b. Because the crime wasn't very serious.
   c. Because she answered all the questions the police officers asked her.
   d. Because the police officers thought Roberta could use her skills somewhere else.
3. What do Roberta's new employers think about people like Roberta?
   a. They should work rather than spend their young years in prison.
   b. They will always make poor choices in life.
   c. They will enjoy working in cyber security.
   d. They are often unfair to people.
4. What is Roberta's job now?
   a. Designing safer websites and servers.
   b. Helping other hackers like her to get a job.
   c. Testing the safety of websites and servers.
   d. Catching dangerous hackers.

I can understand an article about crime and punishments.

What punishment?
Is it possible to commit a crime without knowing it? And if it's true, then what is a fair punishment?

When Roberta was eighteen, a typical school day turned into the most irregular day of her life. To her embarrassment, she was arrested outside her school with all her classmates watching. Her crime was theft. She didn't rob a bank and she wasn't a burglar. She was a hacker and her crime was hacking into her school's records.

But how did Roberta get into hacking? When she was growing up, she had some health problems and she had to spend a lot of time indoors. She thought schoolwork was uninteresting, but she really loved computers. She enjoyed creating programs and doing things that were impossible for others.

After she was arrested, Roberta said she never meant to use the stolen information. She just wanted to test her skills as a hacker. She didn't realise it was illegal. Luckily, the police believed her and had an interesting solution.

Roberta's crime was very serious. But because she wasn't trying to hurt anyone, the police decided to give her a choice. The detectives believed she could have a successful career in cyber security. Roberta could be taken to court and go to prison, or she could start working for a cyber security company.

Roberta did not think twice about it and accepted their offer. Now she works for an IT company who employs young people like her – those who have good computer skills, but have made bad choices in life. The company understands that a prison sentence is too heavy for teenagers. Roberta's job is to stop people from stealing online information. She tries to break into websites and servers to see how they can be improved and protected from attacks in the future.

Roberta earns good money and has a bright future ahead. But do you think it's fair? What punishment would you give Roberta?

8.4 Grammar
have/get something done

GRAMMAR — *have/get something done*

She **has her eyebrows shaped**.
I want to **get my hair cut**.
Are you **going to get your hair dyed**?

1 ● Order the words to make sentences.
1. last summer / had / I / painted / my / bedroom
   I had my bedroom painted last summer.
2. her / suspect / photo / the / taken / had
   _____
3. sofa / can / you / delivered / have / the
   _____
4. where / cleaned / the / you / do / get / car / ?
   _____
5. stolen / his / wallet / last week / he / had
   _____

2 ●● Look at the pictures and complete the sentences with the correct form of the verbs below.

~~get/clean~~   get/cut   get/repair   have/steal   have/take   have/test

1. He needs to *get* his car *cleaned*.
2. He's _____ his eyes _____ at the moment. 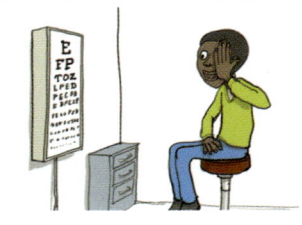
3. They all love _____ their photo _____. 
4. She _____ her bike _____ yesterday. 
5. He needs to _____ his watch _____. 
6. She _____ her hair _____ once a month. 

3 ●● Complete the second sentence using the verbs in brackets so that it means the same as the first one. Use no more than four words.
1. We could ask someone to deliver a pizza if you like. (get)
   We could *get a pizza delivered* if you like.
2. I want someone to cut my hair. (have)
   I want to _____.
3. An expert did her make-up. (had)
   She _____ by an expert.
4. You should ask a doctor to check that injury. (get)
   You should _____ by a doctor.

4 ●●● Complete the text with the correct form of the verbs below.

get/check   get/install   get/put up   have/connect   ~~have/make~~   have/replace

Can you keep your house safe?

Maybe not completely, but security experts think it is worth ¹*having* a few changes *made* to your home to make it safer. A lot of people think that ² _____ a sign _____ saying 'Beware of the dog' is a good idea, but most criminals know that family pets aren't usually dangerous. Locks are important, though. You should ³ _____ any old locks _____ with more modern ones. Modern locks are harder for criminals to open. It's a good idea to ⁴ _____ an alarm _____. You can also ⁵ _____ the alarm _____ to the local police station, so the police are alerted immediately. A good option is to ⁶ _____ your house _____ by a security expert.

Unit 8 **84** I can use the construction *have/get something done*.

On the Portal
Extra Practice Activities: Lesson 8.4

8.5 Listening and Vocabulary
Crimes and criminals

1 **WORD FRIENDS** Complete the text with the words below.

> area   clues   criminal   fingerprints   witnesses

When you get to a crime scene, it's important to search the ^{1}*area* first and look for ^{2}_____. Then you should interview all the ^{3}_____ and take ^{4}_____ of any suspects. When you are sure who is guilty, you can arrest the ^{5}_____ and solve the crime!

2 🔊 **8.1** Listen to a police officer talking about a crime. Order the events.

- a ☐ Sergeant Linfield went to the house.
- b ☐ Police officers took fingerprints and looked for clues.
- c ☐ Sergeant Linfield called the number labelled 'Home'.
- d ☐ Mrs Jones found a mobile phone in the garden.
- e ☐ 1 Mr and Mrs Jones reported a burglary.
- f ☐ Sergeant Linfield caught the burglar.
- g ☐ Sergeant Linfield interviewed Mr and Mrs Jones.

3 🔊 **8.2** Listen to a news report. Complete the notes.

> Place of robbery: ^{1}*post office* on Park Street
> Date of robbery: ^{2}_____
> Amount of money stolen: ^{3}£_____
> Number of suspects: ^{4}_____
> Colour of suspects' car: ^{5}_____
> Number to call if you have information: ^{6}_____

4 🔊 **8.3** Listen to some people talking about crimes. Choose the correct answer.

1 What did the thieves take?
   A ☐   B ☐   C ☐

2 What was Dan doing when the burglary happened?
   A ☐   B ☐   C ☐

3 What did the vandals do last night?
   A ☐   B ☐   C ☐

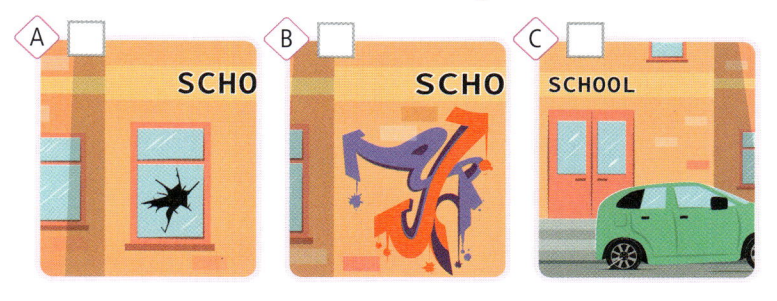

4 What happened at the station?
   A ☐   B ☐   C ☐

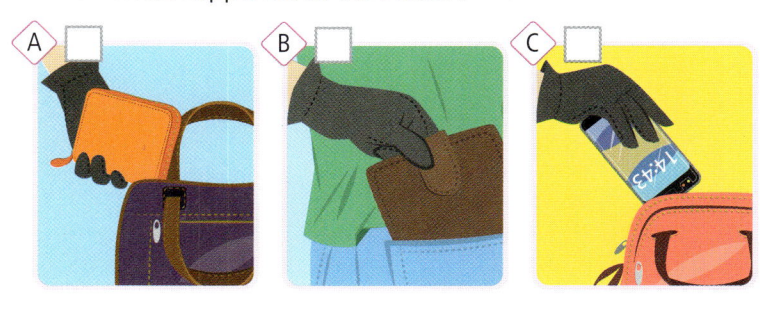

5 Who stole the computer game?
   A ☐   B ☐   C ☐

I can understand people talking about a crime.

8.6 Speaking
Keeping a conversation going

1 🔊 **8.4** Listen and repeat the phrases.

> **SPEAKING** — Keeping a conversation going
>
> **Inviting**
> Are you OK?   Is something wrong?
> Do you want to talk about it?   Go on, tell me.
>
> **Encouraging**
> What do you mean?   Really?   Then what happened?
> I'm sure (you were/did).   Exactly.
>
> **Reassuring**
> Don't worry. I'm fine. Honestly.
> Of course you can (do it).   Right.
>
> **Responding**
> Definitely!   Absolutely!   I don't know.

2 Complete the sentences with one word in each gap.
1 *Come* on! It's always better to discuss things.
2 A: I didn't go to the exam yesterday. Was that a good idea?
   B: I don't _____.
3 Of _____ you can do it! You've worked hard to learn this trick.
4 I see what you _____. The sisters really look very similar.
5 You look sad. Do you want to _____ about it?
6 So you said you were sorry. Then what _____?

3 Match the sentence halves.
1 [e] I don't
2 [ ] Personally,
3 [ ] I'm fine.
4 [ ] Go on,
5 [ ] What do
6 [ ] What's

a Honestly.
b I think she's unkind.
c your opinion?
d tell me.
e ~~think so.~~
f you mean?

4 Choose the correct response.
1 I told her that her behaviour was silly.
   a Go on, tell me.
   (b) Was that a good idea?
   c Of course you can do it.
2 Is something wrong?
   a I'm fine. Honestly.
   b Great. Right …
   c Definitely!
3 Do you agree?
   a Then what happened?
   b Absolutely!
   c Really?
4 I don't know if I should talk about it.
   a I'm fine. Honestly.
   b Do you agree?
   c Go on, tell me!
5 What's your opinion?
   a Come on.
   b Personally, I think he was irresponsible.
   c Are you OK?

5 🔊 **8.5** Complete the dialogue with the words below. There are two extra words. Listen and check.

> course   definitely   happened   mean   opinion
> personally   really   tell   think   ~~wrong~~

Amy: Hi, Sam. Is something ¹*wrong*?
Sam: It's nothing.
Amy: Go on, ² _____ me.
Sam: It's this photo of me that Gemma posted. I think I look bad. What do you ³ _____?
Amy: ⁴ _____, I think you look great. But if you don't like it, you should ask her to remove it.
Sam: I did, but she refused.
Amy: ⁵ _____? What are you going to do next?
Sam: I don't know. What's your ⁶ _____?
Amy: I'd talk to Ms Mason. She'll know what to do.
Sam: I see what you ⁷ _____. Maybe I'll talk to her after the lesson.
Amy: ⁸ _____. I can come with you if you want.
Sam: Thanks, Amy.

On the Portal
Extra Practice Activities: Lesson 8.6

8.7 Writing
An opinion essay

1 Read the article and match paragraphs 1–4 with topics a–d below.

a ☐ Adding contrasting ideas
b ☐ Balancing opinions
c ☐ Summarising and concluding
d ☐ Giving your main reaction

'PEOPLE WHO DON'T RECYCLE SHOULD PAY A FINE.'

Do you agree? Explain your ideas.

1 In my opinion, there are many ways we can help protect the environment and recycling is one of them. Plastic, glass, paper and metal can all easily be recycled and reused. Unfortunately, these things are often thrown away and, as a result, hurt wildlife and nature. But I don't believe that fines are the best solution to the problem.

2 On the one hand, everybody should be responsible when they throw things away. For most people it's easy to recycle, so fines might be a good punishment for people who are too lazy to separate their rubbish. On the other hand, some people would have to travel a long way to do this. For this reason, I think a fine would be an unfair punishment.

3 Although I agree some people should be given a punishment for not recycling, I think that there is a bigger problem to solve. In order to make a difference, big companies need to stop using so much plastic and other unecological materials, and pay big fines if they don't recycle.

4 In general, I think that fines for companies is the best way to stop plastic and other harmful materials being left around in seas and forests.

2 Read the essay again. Mark the sentences T (true) or F (false).
The writer thinks that
1 ☐ recycling is the best way to help the environment.
2 ☐ recycling isn't easy for everyone.
3 ☐ big companies should use no plastic at all.
4 ☐ giving fines to companies is the best way to help the environment.

3 Match the sentence halves.
1 [f] We wrote an email to the supermarket
2 ☐ As a result of crime in the area,
3 ☐ He's going to the police station so
4 ☐ He broke the law, so
5 ☐ They went to the bank in
6 ☐ Pickpocketing is a big problem. For

a there are more security cameras.
b this reason, we need more police officers on the street.
c as to get his reward.
d order to look for clues.
e he has to pay a fine.
f ~~to ask them to use less plastic.~~

WRITING TIME

4 Write an opinion essay on the following question: Young people who damage school building should do community work for school. Do you agree? Explain your ideas.

1 Find ideas
Make notes about:
• your opinion on fines. Are they a good punishment?
• any other ideas to encourage people to behave responsibly.
• your conclusion.

2 Plan and write
• Organise your ideas into paragraphs. Use the essay in Exercise 1 to help you.
• Write a draft essay.

3 Check
• Check language: did you use connectors correctly?
• Check grammar: did you use the passive correctly?
• Write the final version of your essay.

I can write an opinion essay.

My Language File

WORDLIST 🔊 8.6

Criminals
- burglar (n) _____
- pickpocket (n) _____
- robber (n) _____
- shoplifter (n) _____
- thief (n) _____
- vandal (n) _____

Word friends (crime collocations)
- break into homes _____
- break the law _____
- commit a crime _____
- damage buildings _____
- rob a bank _____
- solve crimes _____
- steal things _____

Word building (crimes)
- burglary (n) _____
- pickpocketing (n) _____
- robbery (n) _____
- shoplifting (n) _____
- theft (n) _____
- vandalism (n) _____

Solving crimes
- case (n) _____
- clue (n) _____
- detective (n) _____
- fingerprint (n) _____
- security camera (n) _____
- suspect (n) _____
- witness (n) _____

The law
- court (n) _____
- fine (n) _____
- judge (n) _____
- lawyer (n) _____
- prison (n) _____
- punishment (n) _____
- reward (n) _____
- sentence (n) _____

Word building (negative adjectives)
- illegal (adj) _____
- illogical (adj) _____
- impatient (adj) _____
- impossible (adj) _____
- irregular (adj) _____
- uncomfortable (adj) _____
- unfair (adj) _____
- unhappy (adj) _____
- unimportant (adj) _____
- uninteresting (adj) _____
- unkind (adj) _____
- unusual (adj) _____

Word friends (investigating crimes)
- arrest a criminal _____
- interview a witness _____
- look for clues _____
- search the area _____
- take fingerprints _____

Extra words
- accuse (v) _____
- apology (n) _____
- appear (v) _____
- assistant (n) _____
- author (n) _____
- be in trouble with _____
- catch (v) _____
- chase (v) _____
- choice (n) _____
- community (n) _____
- description (n) _____
- elementary (adj) _____
- engine (n) _____
- eyebrow (n) _____
- fair punishment _____
- fingernail (n) _____
- get away (v) _____
- install (v) _____
- investigate (v) _____
- irresponsible (adj) _____
- jewellery (n) _____
- jury (n) _____
- lie (v) _____
- mind (n) _____
- neighbourhood (n) _____
- politician (n) _____
- publish (v) _____
- purse (n) _____
- question (v) _____
- quote (n) _____
- recording (n) _____
- series (n) _____
- shop window (n) _____
- stone (n) _____
- street light (n) _____
- swing (n) _____
- wallet (n) _____

Sounds good!
- So cute! _____
- Just ignore them! _____
- By the way. _____

MY LANGUAGE NOTES

My favourite words/expressions from this unit

_____
_____
_____
_____
_____
_____
_____
_____
_____
_____

Self-check

Vocabulary

1 Match the words below with the definitions. There is one extra word.

> clue fine judge pickpocketing prison reward
> shoplifter suspect theft vandal witness

1 someone who steals things from shops: _____
2 an amount of money that someone has to pay as a punishment: _____
3 a place where criminals are sent as a punishment: _____
4 someone who damages buildings or things in public places: _____
5 the crime of stealing things: _____
6 someone in court who decides what punishment a criminal should receive: _____
7 a piece of information that is used by the police to solve a crime: _____
8 someone who sees a crime happen: _____
9 the crime of stealing phones or wallets from someone in the street: _____
10 a person who the police think committed a crime: _____

2 Choose the correct option.

1 I don't like sitting on this chair. It's *irregular / uncomfortable*.
2 I couldn't do the homework. One task was *impossible / irresponsible* to complete.
3 That comment was really *unhappy / unkind*. You should say sorry.
4 The boss punished us all for Jim's behaviour. It was so *irregular / unfair*.
5 She never locks the front door at night. It's very *illegal / irresponsible*.

3 Complete the sentences with the words below.

> area clues criminals fingerprints witness

1 The police took his _____ and found they were the same as the ones on the broken window.
2 It is the job of the police to arrest _____.
3 The police are interviewing the _____ to find out what he saw.
4 The police found the watch when they were looking for _____.
5 The police are searching the _____.

Grammar

4 Complete the sentences with the correct passive form of the verbs in brackets.

1 Security cameras _____ (use) in many cities.
2 He _____ (arrest) yesterday for the theft.
3 The money _____ (find) two days later.
4 Crimes _____ (solve) using scientific evidence.
5 The accident last night _____ (not see) by any witnesses.
6 Most criminals _____ (not send) to prison the first time they commit a crime.
7 Usually, criminals _____ (give) a sentence by judges in court.
8 _____ your sister _____ (interview) by the police yesterday?

5 Choose the correct option.

1 We need to get our TV *repair / repaired*.
2 I had *cut my hair / my hair cut* last week.
3 Shall we get *a pizza delivered / delivered a pizza*?
4 He's having a new suit *made / make*.
5 We want to have the carpets *clean / cleaned*.
6 I had my bike *stealing / stolen*.
7 Is the suspect having his fingerprints *took / taken*?

Speaking

6 Complete the dialogue with the words below. There are two extra words.

> fine really see tell that think wrong

A: Hi, Tara. You don't look very happy. Is something ¹_____?
B: I'm ²_____. Honestly.
A: I can tell you're not OK. Go on, ³_____ me.
B: Melissa doesn't want to talk to me. I told her how annoyed I was with being late for the cinema.
A: Was ⁴_____ a good idea? She's having a bad week.
B: I don't think it was unfair. She's always late.
A: I ⁵_____ what you mean.

YOUR SCORE

Vocabulary: __/20   Speaking: __/5
Grammar: __/15   Total: __/40

Lessons in life

9

9.1 Vocabulary
Education

VOCABULARY
School subjects | Describing students | Learning and assessment | Collocations with *make* and *take* | Phrasal verbs

GRAMMAR
Reported speech: statements | Word order in questions

1 ● Look at pictures A–F and write the school subjects.

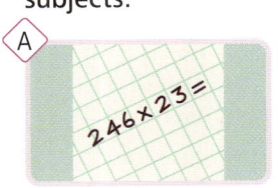

A. Maths
B. _____
C. _____
D. _____
E. _____
F. _____

2 ●● Write the correct school subject for each definition.

1. You read books and plays in this subject.
   L*iterature*
2. You learn about the world and different countries in this subject. G_____
3. You learn about life in this subject. B_____
4. In this subject you discuss how people, businesses and governments use money. E_____
5. You need to study this if you want to be an actor. D_____
6. You study drawing, painting and sculpture in this subject. A_____
7. If you study these, you can talk to people from different countries. L_____
8. You make things from wood in this subject. D_____
9. This is a great subject for people who love sport. P_____
10. If you want to be an astronaut, you have to study this science subject. P_____

3 ●● Complete the sentences with the words below.

| confident | creative | critical | general | hard-working |
| intelligent | problem | ~~talented~~ | teamwork |

1. Emma's so *talented* – she can dance, sing and draw beautifully.
2. Tara's very _____, so she isn't shy when she meets new people.
3. Paul is so _____. I don't know where he gets these great ideas for his stories.
4. The project was difficult, but we didn't ask for help. We practised our _____-solving skills instead.
5. We need Matt in our quiz team because his _____ knowledge is amazing!
6. My little brother is very _____. He's clever and learns fast.
7. We did lots of different tasks in groups of four today to practise _____.
8. Val never stops working until the job is done. She's so _____.
9. I think it's important to learn _____ thinking skills so that you know how to make good decisions.

4 ● Complete the words in the sentences.

1. I find it difficult to l_e_ _a_ _r_n irregular verbs.
2. I usually s____y for about an hour every evening.
3. It's difficult to m__m__ __ __ e a whole poem!
4. I need to r__v__ e for my Maths exam.
5. We have a p__ __c__ c_l e__ __m in Cooking – we have to prepare a meal!
6. That topic isn't on the c__ __ __ c_l__m. We don't need to know it for the test.

Unit 9 90

5 ●● Choose the correct answer.
1. It's going to be a short ___ test, so we can do it from our computers at home.
   a practical   (b) online   c speaking
2. Don't forget: you need to hand in your ___ on Friday.
   a curriculum   b practical exam   c project
3. I'd love to have Film-making on my school ___.
   a curriculum   b presentation   c study
4. The examiner will ask you questions in the English ___ exam.
   a practical   b written   c speaking
5. Are you going to give your ___ to the whole class or just the teacher?
   a presentation   b written exam   c project
6. We get a choice of topics for the essay in our ___.
   a written exam   b presentation   c study

6 ●●● Choose the correct answer to complete the school web page.
1. a memorise   (b) study
   c perform
2. a learn   b revise
   c make
3. a Chemistry   b Physics
   c Cooking
4. a wrote   b writer
   c written
5. a revising   b memorising
   c performing
6. a memorising   b practising
   c getting
7. a facts   b learning
   c knowledge
8. a understanding   b thinking
   c knowledge
9. a problem   b practical
   c general
10. a general   b talented
    c creative
11. a curriculum   b teamwork
    c solving
12. a worked   b working
    c worker

Redfield School

WHO WE ARE

At Redfield School we believe in a modern approach to education. Of course, students here ¹___ traditional subjects such as Maths and History, but they also ²___ more practical skills, such as ³___, which we think are important for life. As well as the main subjects, there are lots of extra classes that students can choose to do, such as Yoga or Fashion Design. We only have ⁴___ exams once a year and we don't expect students to spend a lot of time ⁵___ for them. We believe that old-fashioned methods of learning such as ⁶___ lots of facts aren't important in the modern world. The internet is there to check facts, so people don't need general ⁷___ in the same way that they did in the past. We believe it's more important to teach our students critical ⁸___ skills so they can form their own opinions, and ⁹___-solving so they don't always have to ask for help. We want our students to be ¹⁰___ and use their imagination in everything they do. We also believe that ¹¹___ is a really important skill and we encourage our students to work with each other in groups.
If you are ¹²hard-___ and want to experience an exciting new approach to education, we'd love to have you at Redfield!

I can talk about school life.

9.2 Grammar
Reported speech: statements

> **GRAMMAR** — Reported speech: statements
>
> **Present Simple → Past Simple**
> 'You need a list of interesting topics.'
> Teachers said (that) we needed a list of interesting topics.
>
> **Present Continuous → Past Continuous**
> 'We're starting a debating club.'
> Pupils told their teachers (that) they were starting a debating club.

1 Choose the correct option.
1. 'The students want to start a debating club.'
   Yuki said that the students *want* / *(wanted)* to start a debating club.
2. 'I'm doing my presentation on music.'
   Richard told me that he *is* / *was* doing his presentation on music.
3. 'Harry does a lot of art in his free time.'
   Sinem said Harry *does* / *did* a lot of art in his free time.
4. 'The students aren't working hard enough.'
   The teacher said that the students *aren't* / *weren't* working hard enough.
5. 'Marwan isn't very creative.'
   Tim told me that Marwan *isn't* / *wasn't* very creative.
6. 'Jill is helping them study.'
   Maya said Jill *is* / *was* helping them study.

2 Complete the sentences with *said* or *told*.
1. The teacher *said* that we had to revise for the test.
2. Bruno _____ me how to do the homework.
3. Our drama teacher _____ we had to perform in a play.
4. Leticia _____ us that she wrote about Italy in her project.
5. Alex _____ me that he didn't like teamwork.
6. Claire _____ me she wasn't ready for the test.
7. Chris _____ he ate lunch after the volleyball match.
8. Their Geography teacher _____ them to prepare a presentation in pairs.

3 Complete the reported statements.
1. 'Wei likes Biology.'
   She said that Wei *liked* Biology.
2. 'The exam is starting.'
   The teacher told us that the exam _____.
3. 'Mrs Bright gives lots of homework.'
   Dave said that Mrs Bright _____ lots of homework.
4. 'It isn't raining anymore.'
   Rose said it _____ anymore.
5. 'Phillip isn't revising for the written tests.'
   They told us that Phillip _____ for the written tests.
6. 'I play games on my smartphone every day.'
   She said that she _____ games on her smartphone every day.

4 Choose the correct option.
1. They *said* / *(told)* me it *is* / *(was)* snowing.
2. Anton *said* / *told* that he *was* / *is* on the bus.
3. She *said* / *told* me that she *does* / *did* homework very quickly.
4. Jake *said* / *told* that he *needs* / *needed* more time to write his essay.
5. Alice *said* / *told* us that she *was* / *is* studying hard for the exam.
6. Some students *said* / *told* the exam *is* / *was* too difficult.

5 Rewrite the statements in reported speech.
1. 'I'm writing 3,000 words for my essay,' said Tom.
   Tom said he was writing 3,000 words for his essay.
2. 'Amy doesn't know the answer,' said Kate.
   _____
3. 'Magda works hard in History lessons,' said the teacher.
   _____
4. 'The debate starts at 4.00,' the club president told us.
   _____
5. 'They're making some new posters,' said Luke.
   _____
6. 'Paul isn't speaking very clearly,' said Hannah.
   _____

I can report what people say.

On the Portal
Extra Practice Activities: Lesson 9.2

9.3 Reading and Vocabulary
Learning effectively

1 **WORD FRIENDS** Complete the sentences with *make* or *take*. Sometimes both are possible.
1. I need to *make* progress with my Spanish.
2. When I study I try to _____ a connection between different topics. It helps me remember things.
3. It's a good idea to _____ notes during History lessons, so you've got the important facts written down.
4. I don't understand this sentence – it doesn't _____ sense!
5. You have to _____ an exam when you finish secondary school if you want to go to university.
6. It's important to _____ a break from studying every hour to rest.

2 Read the article quickly and number topics a–d in the order that they are mentioned.
a ☐ Comfortable chairs
b ☐ Changing the lights
c ☐ Classroom temperature
d ☐ Moving desks

3 Read the article again. Complete gaps 1–5 with sentences a–f. There is one extra sentence.
a I like going there to revise, and now I don't have to ask.
b The next day I told my teacher, Mr Cruz, all about it.
c A brighter classroom can make lazy students work harder.
d That's OK, but the light is quite yellow and our eyes get tired.
e They should also be easy to move.
f He agreed to buy some plants instead.

The ultimate classroom

Did you know that the place where you study may make your learning easier? I have read a very interesting report about it. It was found that good classroom design could improve learning, and making small changes can make a big difference. ¹____ He said we could make some improvements to our classroom, so this is what we did.

First of all, it seems that temperature is very important. Classrooms shouldn't be too hot or too cold. Mr Cruz said that it's not possible to change the heating in school. ²____ They make the room look nice and they also clean the air.

The researchers also said that students work best when they are given choices. Mr Cruz agreed that during some activities we could choose where we want to work. We usually sit at desks to make notes, take tests or plan presentations. But we also have comfortable chairs and a sofa at the back of the classroom. ³____

What's more, the researchers believe that the best desks were round. ⁴____ When the lesson includes teamwork or project work, students should sit face to face and chairs or desks have to be moved. For individual work, it's good to create more space between students so they can focus on their tasks.

The last thing I read about was lights. Research showed that natural light was best, but unfortunately, my classroom only has small windows. That means we have the lights on all the time. ⁵____ Mr Cruz said he was going to get the lights changed to ones which give more natural light. I think that's a great idea.

With all these changes, I think we'll make great progress this year. I'm quite excited and I'm looking forward to our written exam next month to see the results!

I can understand an article about effective learning.

9.4 Grammar
Word order in questions

GRAMMAR — Word order in questions

Yes/No questions
It is OK. → **Is** it OK?
You have done some online courses. → **Have** you done any online courses?
You enjoyed it. → **Did** you enjoy it?

Wh- questions
Why are you laughing?
Why do you ask so many questions?

Subject questions
A: Who **studied** with you?   B: Lee studied with me.

Object questions
A: Who **did** you **study** with?   B: I studied with Lee.

1 Choose the correct option.
1 (Why) / What is Ted upset?
2 How / When do your online lessons start?
3 Who / What are you going to invite to your party?
4 What / Where does the performance take place?

2 Order the words to make questions.
1 you / OK / are / ?
   Are you OK?
2 live / where / you / do / ?
   _____
3 you / book / did / enjoy / the / ?
   _____
4 Sam's / have / met / you / brother / ?
   _____

3 Read the sentences. Complete the question to match the answer.
1 Ellie and Jo told me about the party.
   A: Who *told you about the party*?
   B: Ellie and Jo.
2 Sam gave me this card.
   A: What _____?
   B: This card.
3 Anna phoned me last night.
   A: Who _____?
   B: Me.
4 Tom helped me with my homework.
   A: What _____?
   B: My homework.

4 Read the answers. Complete the questions.
1 A: *Is it raining* now?
   B: No, it isn't raining now.
2 A: Where _____?
   B: Rosie goes to school in Manchester.
3 A: When _____?
   B: The film finished at eight o'clock.
4 A: Who _____?
   B: Mrs Cavendish teaches them French.
5 A: Who _____?
   B: She phoned Carl.

5 Complete the dialogue. Make questions using the words in brackets.
Rob: Hi, Dad. ¹*What are you doing* (what/you/do)?
Dad: I'm just looking at some old photos from school.
Rob: ² _____ (it/be/OK) if I take a look?
Dad: Sure it's fine.
Rob: ³ _____ (who/take/these photos)?
Dad: I can't remember who took them.
Rob: Wow! It looks very different from my school. ⁴ _____ (what/subjects/you/study)?
Dad: Oh, we studied all the usual subjects.
Rob: ⁵ _____ (you/enjoy/school)?
Dad: Not really. We didn't do many fun activities like you do.
Rob: ⁶ _____ (what/your teachers/be/like)?
Dad: They were very strict!
Rob: ⁷ _____ (who/that/be)?
Dad: My best friend, Tom. We got on really well.
Rob: He looks cool. ⁸ _____ (you/stay/friends) with him since you left school?
Dad: No, I haven't. He went to the USA and I haven't heard from him for years.

I can make questions with the correct word order.

On the Portal
Extra Practice Activities: Lesson 9.4

9.5 Listening and Vocabulary
Conversations in the classroom

1 Complete the sentences with the correct form of the phrasal verbs below.

> calm down   fill in   get on   hand in   hand out
> look over   look up   ~~miss out~~

1. If you do your homework now, you won't _miss out_ on football practice later.
2. The teacher wants us to _____ our projects on Friday, but I haven't started mine yet!
3. Remember to leave time at the end of the exam to _____ all your answers.
4. _____! There's nothing to be upset or angry about.
5. I keep my dictionary with me, so I can _____ words that I don't know.
6. It's time to stop playing computer games and _____ with your homework!
7. You have to _____ a form to join the gym.
8. Tanya, please _____ these books – one book to every pair of students.

2 🔊 9.1 Choose the correct answer. Listen and check.

1. Have you all finished the first exercise?
   a Yes, we are.
   b Not quite, Mr Cowen.
   c No, we didn't.
2. Did you manage to answer all the questions in the test?
   a No, I didn't.
   b Yes, you have.
   c No, they aren't.
3. Could you lend me a pen, please?
   a No, I don't.
   b Yes, I have.
   c Of course.
4. How long did you spend on your Maths homework?
   a About an hour.
   b No, I didn't spend any.
   c For half an hour.

3 🔊 9.2 Listen to some people talking about school life. Choose the correct answer.

1. What did the teacher catch the girl doing in class?
   A ☐   B ☐   C ☐

2. Who did the boy write a text to?
   A ☐   B ☐   C ☐

3. Why is the girl late for school?
   A ☐   B ☐   C ☐

4. What happened to the boy at the school play?
   A ☐   B ☐   C ☐

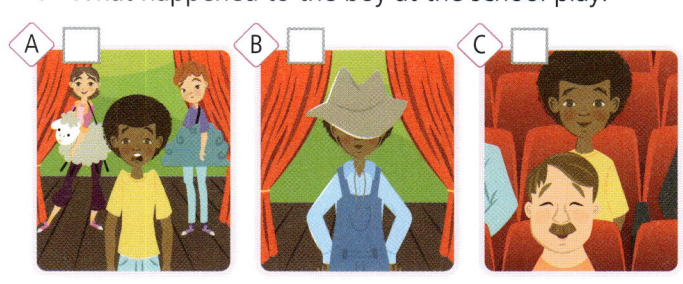

5. What has the girl lost?
   A ☐   B ☐   C ☐

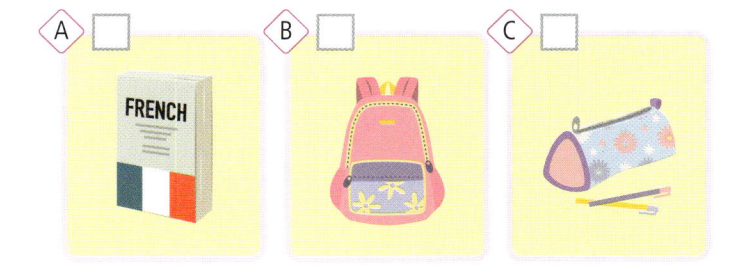

I can understand short classroom conversations.

9.6 Speaking
Exchanging information

1 🔊 **9.3** Listen and repeat the phrases.

> **SPEAKING** — **Exchanging information**
>
> **Past experience**
> Have you been in England before?
>
> **Present situation**
> Where are you from?
> How long are you staying for?
> What do you think of the UK?
>
> **Future plans**
> What are you (guys) doing now/later?
> Would you like to get an ice cream?

2 Complete the questions with one word in each gap.
1 _Where_ are you from?
2 What _____ you doing this evening?
3 How _____ are you staying for?
4 What _____ you think of the city?
5 _____ you been in the USA before?
6 _____ you like to get a coffee?

3 Choose the correct response.
1 Have you been in London before?
  a Yes, I did.
  b I didn't go to London.
  c No, it's my first time here.
2 Would you like to come with us?
  a I'd love to.
  b No, I don't, thanks.
  c Yes, I love it.
3 What are you doing at the weekend?
  a I didn't enjoy it.
  b I'm fine, thanks.
  c I'm going to a party.
4 How long are you staying for?
  a Thanks, that would be great.
  b For three weeks.
  c In a hotel.
5 What do you think of the UK?
  a No way!
  b It's great.
  c Not really.

4 Match questions 1–6 with responses a–f.
1 _e_ How long are you staying for?
2 ___ What do you think of the UK?
3 ___ Have you been in Scotland before?
4 ___ Would you like to get some pizza?
5 ___ What are you doing now?
6 ___ Where are you from?

a We're going to get some hot chocolate.
b France. Have you ever been there?
c Well, it's nice, but it's quite cold.
d Oh yes, I'm really hungry.
e ~~Only for the weekend.~~
f Yes, but it was a long time ago.

5 🔊 **9.4** Complete the dialogue with one word in each gap. Listen and check.

Rory: Oh there's Tara, a friend of mine. Tara, over here!
Tara: Hi.
Rory: Tara, this is Elsa. She's a friend of mine from back home.
Tara: Nice to meet you, Elsa. Have you ¹_been_ to Edinburgh before?
Elsa: No, this is my first time.
Tara: Wow! What do you ²_____ of the city?
Elsa: Oh, it's beautiful!
Tara: Yeah, I love it too. How long are you staying ³_____?
Elsa: I'm here for one week. Tara, where are you ⁴_____?
Tara: I'm from Devon, in the south of England. So, what are you guys ⁵_____ this evening?
Rory: We're going for a pizza. Would you ⁶_____ to join us?
Tara: I'd love to. Thanks!

Unit 9 | 96 | I can exchange information in a conversation.

On the Portal
Extra Practice Activities: Lesson 9.6

9.7 Writing
A formal letter asking for information

1 Read the advert and Luca's letter. Mark the sentences T (true) or F (false).
1. ☐ Luca wants to do an online English course.
2. ☐ Luca is planning a trip to the UK.
3. ☐ Luca wants to know how big the groups are.
4. ☐ Luca wants to improve his speaking skills.
5. ☐ Luca wants to learn about different English-speaking countries.

Online English courses
Would you like to improve your language skills?
Do you want to learn from the comfort of your own home? We have a range of English courses that are perfect for you.

Write to us for more information.

75 Via Roma,
Florence 50123
Italy

25th January

① Dear Mrs Langton,

② I am ¹*writing* to ask about the online intensive English course for teenagers. I would like to prepare for my school exams and this course could help me a lot.

③ Would you ² _____ giving me some information about how the online classes work? In particular, do we meet every day at the same time, or can I watch the lessons in my own time? Please could you also ³ _____ me how long the lessons are and how much they cost?

④ My English teacher told me that my speaking skills are very good, but I need to improve my writing and grammar. My ⁴ _____ is to do as much writing as possible and I would like some help me with this. I also hope to learn about different English-speaking countries around the world.

⑤ I look ⁵ _____ to your reply.

⑥ Yours sincerely,
Luca Porta

2 Read Luca's letter again and complete it with the words below.

aim   forward   mind   tell   ~~writing~~

3 Match sentences 1–6 with functions a–f.
1. [d] Please could you send me some information?
2. ☐ Yours sincerely,
3. ☐ I am writing to say that I am interested in your summer course.
4. ☐ Dear Mr Gallagher,
5. ☐ My plan is to work in the UK next year.
6. ☐ I look forward to hearing from you soon.

a ending your letter
b giving information
c greeting
d ~~asking for information~~
e before you finish
f saying why you are writing

WRITING TIME

4 Imagine you want to take an online English course. Write a letter in response to the advert, asking for information.

1 Find ideas
Make notes about:
- questions you would like to ask.
- information you will give.
- your learning goals.

2 Plan and write
- Organise your ideas into paragraphs. Use Luca's letter to help you.
- Write a draft letter.

3 Check
- Check language: did you use a range of phrases to talk about your learning goals?
- Check grammar: is the word order in questions correct?
- Write the final version of your letter.

I can write a formal letter asking for information.

My Language File

WORDLIST 🔊 9.5

School subjects
- Art (n) ___
- Biology (n) ___
- Chemistry (n) ___
- Cooking (n) ___
- Drama (n) ___
- D&T (Design and Technology) (n) ___
- Economics (n) ___
- Geography (n) ___
- History (n) ___
- IT (Information Technology) (n) ___
- Languages (n) ___
- Literature (n) ___
- Maths (n) ___
- Music (n) ___
- PE (Physical Education) (n) ___
- Physics (n) ___

Describing students
(qualities of a good student)
- confident (adj) ___
- creative (adj) ___
- hard-working (adj) ___
- intelligent (adj) ___
- talented (adj) ___

(skills)
- critical thinking (n) ___
- general knowledge (n) ___
- problem-solving (n) ___
- teamwork (n) ___

Learning
- curriculum (n) ___
- learn (v) ___
- memorise (v) ___
- revise (v) ___
- study (v) ___

Types of assessment
- online test (n) ___
- practical exam (n) ___
- presentation (n) ___
- project (n) ___
- speaking exam (n) ___
- written exam (n) ___

Word friends (learning)
- make a connection ___
- make/take notes ___
- make progress ___
- make sense ___
- take a break ___
- take a test ___
- take an exam ___

Phrasal verbs
- calm down (v) ___
- fill in (a form) (v) ___
- get on (v) ___
- hand in (v) ___
- hand out (v) ___
- look over (v) ___
- look up (v) ___
- miss out (v) ___

Extra words
- aim (n) ___
- bee-keeping (n) ___
- Citizenship (n) ___
- classroom (n) ___
- club president (n) ___
- course (n) ___
- culture (n) ___
- cyber security (n) ___
- debate (n) ___
- discovery (n) ___
- driving (n) ___
- environment (n) ___
- fashion design (n) ___
- final term (n) ___
- food preparation (n) ___
- fresh place (n) ___
- gardening (n) ___
- goal (n) ___
- head teacher (n) ___
- high school (n) ___
- host family (n) ___
- Humanities (n) ___
- karate (n) ___
- look forward to (v) ___
- member (n) ___
- option (n) ___
- photograph (n) ___
- popular (adj) ___
- pupil (n) ___
- research (n) ___
- Science (n) ___
- special lesson (n) ___
- speech (n) ___
- spidergram (n) ___
- stay calm ___
- store information ___
- suitable (adj) ___
- surfing (n) ___
- traditional dance (n) ___
- university (n) ___
- vocational (adj) ___

Sounds good!
- I can't wait! ___
- You guessed it. ___
- What a coincidence! ___

MY LANGUAGE NOTES

My favourite words/expressions from this unit

Self-check

Vocabulary

1 Complete the sentences with the words below.

> confident   critical   general   IT   memorise
> presentation   revise   speaking   talented
> teamwork

1. Our teacher says that doing projects together helps us to develop _____ thinking.
2. What's the best way to _____ for exams?
3. I don't feel very _____ about the exam. I think it's going to be very difficult.
4. We are designing apps in our _____ class at the moment.
5. I don't know the capital of New Zealand – my _____ knowledge isn't very good.
6. Ricky doesn't like working on his own – he prefers _____.
7. You must _____ this number – I don't have a pen to write it down.
8. What I like about our class is that everybody is so _____ – we all have different skills.
9. I don't mind _____ exams – you often talk about interesting topics.
10. That _____ was so boring. There were no pictures to look at.

2 Choose the correct option.

1. The experiment *makes / takes* a connection between sleep and memory.
2. This paragraph doesn't *make / take* sense.
3. I feel I've *made / taken* a lot of progress with my English this year!
4. If you don't *make / take* a break, you'll get very tired.
5. The teacher said I had to *make / take* an extra test if I wanted to go to university abroad.

3 Complete the sentences with the correct prepositions.

1. You need to fill _____ this form.
2. Calm _____. Everything will be fine.
3. Have you handed _____ your project yet?
4. I'm trying to look _____ this word, but I can't find it in the dictionary.
5. Betty is really sad she missed _____ on the school trip.

Grammar

4 Choose the correct option.

1. She said the exam *is / was* starting soon.
2. Jan *told / said* that presentations were easy to write.
3. He told me that the teacher often *is giving / gives* good grades.
4. Rebecca told *we / us* the competition was starting soon.
5. He said the homework *was / will be* due the following day.
6. Andy said that he *was writing / writes* a presentation.
7. The teacher told us that the lesson *started / start* at 10.00.

5 Complete the questions with the correct form of the verbs in brackets.

1. _____ (you/watch) that programme about physics on TV last night?
2. _____ (he/go) to school by bus?
3. _____ (you/finish) reading yet?
4. _____ (why/Carrie/be) upset last Monday in PE?
5. _____ (who/call) the police last night?
6. _____ (who/you/see) yesterday?
7. _____ (who/do) the most work in your class?
8. _____ (why/you/stand) outside?

Speaking

6 Complete the dialogue with the phrases below.

> have you been   how long   what are   where are   would you

A: Hi. Nice to meet you. ¹_____ you from?
B: I'm from Berlin. Nice to meet you too.
A: ²_____ are you staying for?
B: Just a few weeks.
A: ³_____ in Spain before?
B: Yes, I was here last year. It's great.
A: ⁴_____ you doing now?
B: I'm not sure. I have a lesson in one hour.
A: ⁵_____ like to get a lemonade?
B: Sure! Thanks.

YOUR SCORE

Vocabulary: __/20   Speaking: __/5
Grammar: __/15   Total: __/40

Reading Time 3

The Professor

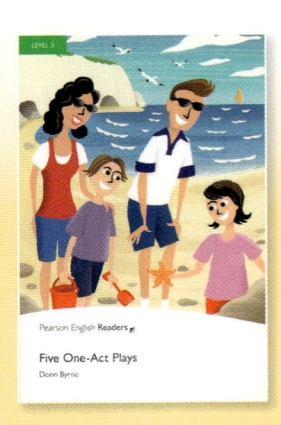

Characters:
Professor Hunter, Mary Hunter, Miss Green, Dr Pitt, Mr Rose, Inspector Hadley, Sergeant Bull

Scene 1

(Mary Hunter *is in her father's room, talking to* Miss Green, *the professor's secretary. It is a large, pleasant room, with a lot of books in it. There is a big desk near the window.*)

Mary Dad's very excited this morning, Miss Green. He didn't want his breakfast. He only had a cup of coffee.

Miss Green Yes, of course he's excited. I'm excited too. This is a very important day. He's ready to give his invention to the world. The papers are complete. I've just copied them.

Mary The men from the government will be here soon, won't they? They'll take the papers to London.

Scene 3

(*It is about eleven o'clock.* The Professor *is still looking at the papers on his desk.* Miss Green *runs into the room.*)

Miss Green Professor! Those two men! Have they left?

Professor (*Looking up*) Yes, of course they've left, Miss Green. They've taken the papers and they've gone back to London.

Miss Green Oh, that's terrible!

Professor What's terrible? What are you talking about?

Miss Green (*Beginning to cry*) They were the wrong men, Professor!

Professor I don't understand. You looked at their cards, didn't you?

Miss Green Yes, but they stole those cards.

Professor How do you know?

Miss Green The police telephoned. The right men were coming from London. These men stopped the car. They locked the men in an empty house and stole all their papers. And now they've stolen your invention. What are we going to do?

(*At that minute the doorbell rings.*)

Professor Go and open the door, Miss Green. It's probably the police.

(Miss Green *goes out of the room. She comes back with two police officers.*)

Inspector I'm Inspector Hadley, sir. And this is Sergeant Bull.

Professor Please sit down.

(*The two policemen sit down.* Inspector Hadley *puts his hat on the Professor's desk.*)

Inspector So those men have taken your papers. Your secretary's told us. But if you describe the men, Professor, we'll try to catch them.

Professor It isn't necessary, Inspector.

Inspector Not necessary? I don't understand, sir. These men have stolen your invention, haven't they?

Professor Oh, the papers aren't very important.

Miss Green What are you saying, Professor? You've worked hard. You wanted to give your invention to the country. Now these men will sell it and make money.

Professor Yes, I worked hard. That's true. But those two men won't sell my invention.

Inspector Why not?

Professor Because I didn't give it to them!

Miss Green Oh!

Professor I'll explain. When I saw the men, I didn't like the look of them. You saw their cards, Miss Green, but I had to be sure. I couldn't give my invention to the wrong men, could I?

Inspector So what did you do?

Professor Well, only one or two very important people know about my invention. When I asked Dr Pitt about it, he knew all about it. I thought that was strange.

Inspector What happened next?

Professor I gave Dr Pitt some old papers. He read them and he accepted them. So he didn't know about my invention. I knew he wasn't the right man.

Inspector So you've still got the papers?

Professor Yes, they're on my desk. They were there all the time.

Inspector But we must try to catch those men, Professor. Can you describe them to us?

Professor (*He thinks.*) Dr Pitt was short and fat. And he had no hair.

Miss Green No, Professor. That was Mr Rose. Dr Pitt was tall and thin.

Professor Are you sure? Well, perhaps you're right. I can't remember things like that.

Inspector (*Standing up*) Don't worry, Professor. Miss Green will describe the men for us.

(*The police sergeant stands up too. They go to the door.*)

Unit 9

Before you read

1 Match sentences 1–4 with pictures A–D.
1 The papers describe how the invention works.
2 The men showed their cards when they arrived.
3 The man is locked in a house.
4 The police want to catch the man.

2 Look at the book cover and read Scene 1. What do you think happens in the story?

While you read

3 🔊 RT3.1 Read and listen to the story. Mark the sentences T (true) or F (false).
1 ☐ Men from the government take the professor's papers.
2 ☐ The men show their cards to Miss Green.
3 ☐ The professor gives information about his invention to the men.
4 ☐ Only a few people know about the invention.
5 ☐ The professor can describe the men to the police.

4 Read the story again. Number events a–e in the order that they happen.
a ☐ The criminals leave.
b ☐ The police arrive.
c ☐ The criminals lock the right men in an empty house.
d ☐ Miss Green runs into the room.
e ☐ The professor tries to describe the two men.

5 Choose the correct answer.
1 The professor doesn't have breakfast because ____.
   a he's very sad   b he's too excited
   c he doesn't have time
2 Miss Green thinks what's happened is ____.
   a exciting   b necessary   c terrible
3 The two men who came to the house were ____.
   a criminals   b professors
   c men from the government
4 The professor thought it was ____ that Dr Pitt knew so much about his invention.
   a clever   b strange   c interesting
5 It's ____ for the professor to describe the men.
   a impossible   b easy   c difficult

After you read

6 Find adjectives from the text with the same meaning.
1 finished _____
2 very bad _____
3 the opposite of *full* _____
4 when you know something is true or correct _____
5 unusual or surprising _____

7 Rewrite the sentences in reported speech.
1 Mary: Dad's very excited this morning, Miss Green.
   Mary told Miss Green that _____.
2 Mary: The men from the government are coming soon.
   Mary said that _____.
3 Professor: I can't remember things like that.
   The professor said that _____.

8 **WRAP UP** Complete the information about the story.

Title: _____
Type: *love story / horror story / crime story*
Main characters: _____
Important object: _____
My opinion: ☆☆☆☆☆

101 Unit 9

Exam Time 1 Listening   Units 1–3

1 🔊 **ET1–3.1** Listen and choose the correct answer.

> **Exam tip**
> You will hear the recording twice.
> The first time, listen and choose your answer.
> The second time, check your answers carefully.

1 What did the boy do at the weekend?
   A ☐   B ☐   C ☐

2 What's the view from the girl's window?
   A ☐   B ☐   C ☐

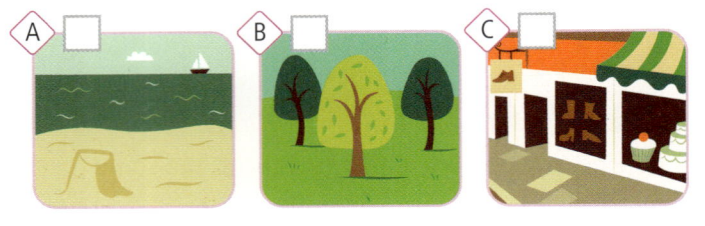

3 What was the weather like yesterday?
   A ☐   B ☐   C ☐

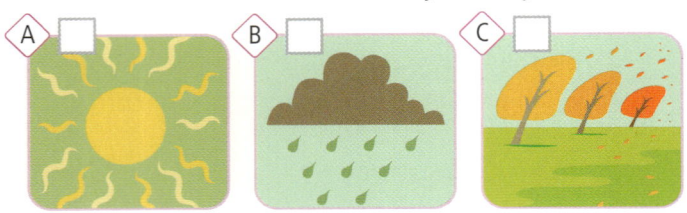

4 What did the boy cook for dinner?
   A ☐   B ☐   C ☐

5 Where is the girl's phone?
   A ☐   B ☐   C ☐

6 What is the boy's sister's job?
   A ☐   B ☐   C ☐

2 🔊 **ET1–3.2** Listen to a teacher talking about a school trip to a science exhibition. Complete the notes with the missing information.

> **Exam tip**
> You will need to complete each gap with a single word, a short phrase, a name or a number.

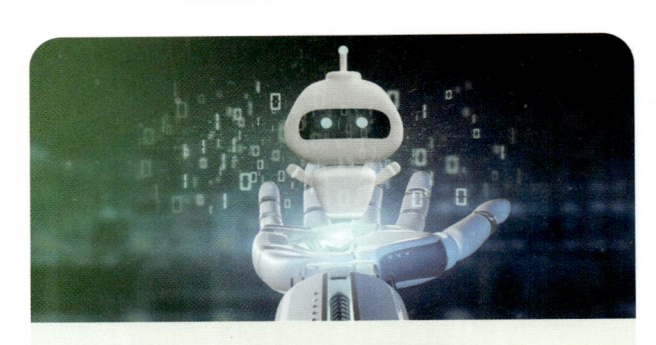

VISIT TO SCIENCE EXHIBITION
Day of trip: [1] *next Thursday*
Name of exhibition: [2] _____
You can have a conversation with a robot called: [3] _____
Trip begins at: [4] _____ a.m.
Coach arrives back at school at: [5] _____ p.m.
Students should take: [6] _____

3 🔊 **ET1–3.3** Two friends are talking about a meal they are going to cook. Listen and match ingredients 1–5 with the ways of preparing them a–h. There are three extra ways that you do not need.

INGREDIENTS		PREPARATION	
1	☐ chicken	a	boiled
2	☐ sweet potato	b	frozen
3	☐ pineapple	c	raw
4	☐ garlic	d	sauce
5	☐ peaches	e	fried
		f	grilled
		g	fresh
		h	roasted

4 🔊 **ET1–3.4** Listen. Then listen again and write down what you hear during each pause.

> **Exam tip**
> The first time you listen, don't try to write too much. Just listen and note down any key words you hear.

Exam Time 1 — Reading and Writing — Units 1–3

5 Read the texts and choose the correct answer.

Exam tip
When you read the texts, underline any words you expect to see in the pictures.

Today's specials
- Tomato soup
- Roast chicken and potatoes
- Peaches and ice cream

1 What are today's specials?

A ☐ B ☐ C ☐

Mum, I left my charging cable for my phone at home. Can you bring it when you pick me up? It's on my desk, connected to my power bank. Thanks!

2 Where is the charging cable?

A ☐ B ☐ C ☐

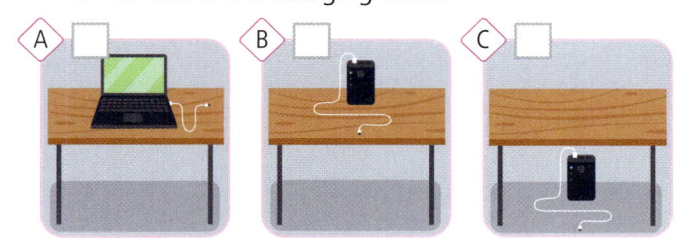

In this week's Wild Weather magazine:

Pages 4–5	**Sunshine:** is it as good for us as we think it is?
Pages 6–12	**Our hurricane special!** Photos, stories and more. Everything you need to know about hurricanes.
Pages 30–31	**Your photos of wild weather.** We print the five best this week.

3 What can readers send in?

A ☐ B ☐ C ☐

PHONE MESSAGE
To: Paul   From: The Pizza Place

The pizza restaurant phoned. They've made a mistake with their bookings, so your table is now for 6.00 p.m., not 7.00 p.m. Call them if the earlier time is a problem because of your work.

4 Why might Paul call the restaurant?

A ☐ B ☐ C ☐

Rosedal School Tech Show
Welcome to our Tech Show. We start at 10 a.m., when you are invited to the main hall to look at examples of the latest technology. In the afternoon, there will be various tasks, where you can meet our student designers. In the evening, please join us in the main hall for a party.

5 What's happening in the morning?

A ☐ B ☐ C ☐

QUICHE
Cook the quiche in the oven for 40 mins. Serve with salad and boiled or roast potatoes.

6 Which option is NOT suggested in the magazine?

A ☐ B ☐ C ☐

Exam Time 1 — Reading and Writing — Units 1–3

6 Read the text and choose the correct answer.

Wild places

More and more people now ¹____ visiting wild places for their holidays. Trips to hot deserts or ²____ cold northern countries are becoming more and more popular. A lot of places that were ³____ difficult to get to in the past are now only a plane ride away. Scientists too are studying the wild places of the world, hoping to ⁴____ new and unusual plants and animals. Of course, tourists who visit these places do their best not to cause any damage and they certainly don't mean to harm the natural world. They just want to experience the natural beauty of the places and take photos that they can share with their friends.

But is tourism killing these wild places that we love so much? They have remained in a natural state ⁵____ thousands of years. Do we really want to change this and turn them into holiday resorts? So, before you ⁶____ the decision to go to one of the world's wild places, maybe you should stop and think. If you haven't been there ⁷____, maybe it's best to stay away.

1	a choose	b enjoy	c decide
2	a cool	b freezing	c mild
3	a really	b completely	c absolutely
4	a look	b find out	c discover
5	a for	b since	c yet
6	a do	b get	c make
7	a ever	b yet	c just

7 Read the article and complete the sentences. Use 1–3 words from the text in each gap.

1 Taste of Chicago is a big *food festival*.
2 The festival happens once _____.
3 At the festival, you can try different types of food, listen to _____ and go on rides.
4 Typical food from Chicago includes an ice cream cone with _____ on top of it.
5 At the festival, people from a big _____ make dishes from their country mixed with American ingredients.
6 The first Taste of Chicago festival took place in _____.

TASTE of Chicago ★★★★★

Taste of Chicago is the largest food festival in the world. It takes place in Grant Park, Chicago, for five days once a year. It's in July and entrance is free to the public. Despite its name, the festival is not just about food. For five days a year, the park comes alive with live music performed by famous artists and fairground rides.

The food includes typical dishes from Chicago, such as the famous deep dish pizza (a pizza with a thick base), seafood and the 'rainbow cone' – an ice cream cone with several different flavours such as chocolate, strawberry and vanilla, topped with cherries and nuts. It's not just food from Chicago, though. There is a large Polish community in Chicago and they offer a unique American flavour to traditional Polish dishes, such as potato, cheese and jalapeño (a type of chilli) dumplings.

The festival started in 1980 and in that year the organisers expected 100,000 people to come. In fact, over 250,000 people came! It has grown over the years and nowadays you can expect crowds of several million people over the week.

8 Read this advert from an English-language website and write an article.

EXAM TIP
Plan your answer carefully before you write so that you make sure you include all the necessary information.

Your favourite dish:

What is your favourite traditional dish from your country?

When do you usually eat this dish? Why?

Write an article in 100 words and we'll put it on our website!

Exam Time 2 Listening Units 1–6

1 🔊 **ET1–6.1** Listen and choose the correct answer.

1. What did the girl watch last night?
   - a a documentary
   - b a talent show
   - c a show about food
2. Where was the boy first at the leisure centre?
   - a at the reception desk
   - b in the café
   - c in the swimming pool
3. What does the girl want to get in town?
   - a a sleeping bag
   - b some money
   - c a tent
4. What type of holiday did the boy go on last year?
   - a sightseeing holiday
   - b backpacking holiday
   - c camping trip
5. What does the girl want to do?
   - a take part in a race
   - b support a team
   - c volunteer at a sports event

2 🔊 **ET1–6.2** Listen to an interview with a girl who has just got a part in a film. Choose the correct answer.

1. How is Suzy feeling at the moment?
   - a worried that it may be too hard
   - b excited about starting work
   - c surprised that she got the part
2. Suzy won't be swimming in the film because
   - a she can't swim.
   - b her character doesn't swim much.
   - c she hasn't got a good style.
3. What sort of film had she been in before?
   - a a comedy
   - b a historical film
   - c an educational film
4. Why didn't Suzy go to drama school?
   - a She got a part in a play.
   - b She wasn't accepted by a drama school.
   - c Her parents advised her to do it later.
5. How does Suzy think she'll change because of the film?
   - a She'll become more confident.
   - b She'll be a better actress.
   - c She'll learn more about jobs in film-making.
6. When the filming ends, Suzy
   - a would like to do some travelling.
   - b will start another film.
   - c is going to drama school.

3 🔊 **ET1–6.3** Listen to some information about a music festival. Complete the notes with the missing information.

> **Exam tip**
> You may hear several pieces of information that sound like the right answer (e.g. different dates), but only one of them is correct. Listen carefully before you write your answer.

Music in the Park
Dates of festival: [1] *9 and 10 August*
Parking: [2] _____ *entrance*
Singers: [3] _____
Dance competition categories:
hip-hop, salsa and [4] _____
Winners will appear on TV show: [5] _____
Book here for cheaper tickets: [6] _____

4 🔊 **ET1–6.4** Listen. Then listen again and write down what you hear during each pause.

Exam Time 2 — Reading and Writing — Units 1–6

5 Read the texts and answer the questions with *J* (Jaden), *C* (Cameron) or *H* (Haley).

> **Exam tip**
> Read each question carefully first, so you know exactly what information to look for in the text.

1 Who started their sport when they were young?
2 Who started their sport because they wanted to have a more healthy lifestyle?
3 Who talks about future study plans?
4 Who is going to take part in a competition next month?
5 Who doesn't spend as much time with their friends as they'd like to?
6 Who talks about how their diet helps them with their sport?
7 Who started their sport recently?

YOUNG SPORTSPEOPLE

Jaden Bishop
I just started running this year. Last year I was unhealthy, eating too much junk food and not getting enough exercise. One day I decided that I needed to do something about it. So I bought some running trainers and started. I was very slow at first and couldn't run very far, but then I improved. Last month I took part in my first race – 5 km – and I finished and got a medal. Next month I'm taking part in my first 10 km race.

Cameron McCoy
I started playing tennis when I was just six years old. When I was ten, I started having lessons and then I entered competitions. Nowadays I train three times a week after school at my local tennis club. It's hard work and I don't have as much of a social life as I want because I train so much, but last year I became county champion. This year I'm going to enter the national competitions because I really want to become national champion!

Haley Mason
I play football with my local girls' football team. I love football. My parents always say I live, breathe and eat it! That's true because I also eat healthily. I try to eat as much fresh fruit and vegetables as I can because it helps me build my strength to help me play. Women's football is big in the USA, and I'd really like to go to university there so I can play more football. If I do well in my exams at school, I'll be able to study there.

6 Read the article and choose the correct answer.

> **Exam tip**
> All three options may use vocabulary from the text. Read each of the options very carefully to see which one exactly matches what the text says.

1 What is Emma trying to do in this text?
   a encourage other people to become circus performers
   b explain why she chose to join a circus
   c explain how to become a circus performer
   d describe her life as a circus performer
2 Emma started training when
   a she was four years old.
   b her parents told her she was old enough.
   c she realised she needed to learn basic skills.
   d her cousins saw how talented she was.
3 What does Emma not enjoy about her way of life?
   a Travelling around a lot is very tiring.
   b It's difficult to make new friends.
   c It can be boring to do the same show every day.
   d It can be difficult working and living with the same people.
4 How does Emma feel about her education?
   a She doesn't think it's necessary.
   b She would prefer to go to a school.
   c She knows it's necessary.
   d She thinks her career in the circus is more important.
5 What might Emma say about her life?
   a 'I didn't really choose this life, but now I love it.'
   b 'I'd love to do something different if I had the choice.'
   c 'I don't enjoy training, but I love performing.'
   d 'It's impossible to enjoy this way of life.'

Exam Time 2 — Reading and Writing — Units 1–6

THE CIRCUS
by Emma Jenkins

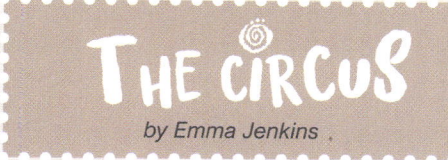

People often ask me what it's like to be a circus performer. I grew up in a circus family, so I've always watched the performances and I never questioned the fact that I would grow up to be part of the show.

I decided when I was four years old that I wanted to be a trapeze artist with my cousins, flying through the air high above everyone's heads. I wanted to start training immediately, but my parents thought I was too young. A year later, I was playing with my cousins and they showed me a few basic skills. They quickly saw that I was a natural performer, so they asked my parents to allow me to start training, even though I was still young.

Although I love performing and each day brings something different, it isn't all fun. For a start, we move to a new place every two weeks. This isn't as tiring as it sounds because we get time off to rest during the day, but it means that it isn't easy to meet new people and form friendships. Of course, our family members are also our friends, and it's great to train, perform and live with the same people.

I don't go to school, but my mum gives me lessons and I also study on my own. I study everything in the national guidelines so I can take the national exams. Although it's hard to find the time, I know that I need to be disciplined because it's just as important as my performing career. After all, I may need to find a different job one day.

I know that my life is unusual, and it was something I was born to, not something I chose. I sometimes think about doing something different, but somehow the daily routine of training and performing is in my blood. I find it impossible to think of anything I would enjoy more.

7 Read the advert and answer the questions.

1. Where do you need to live to upgrade to VITA Plus membership? <u>Hounslow</u>
2. How much does it cost to upgrade to VITA Plus membership? _____
3. What class doesn't it let you do for free? _____
4. What event can you take a friend to for free? _____

VITA Gyms – VITA Plus membership

VITA Plus membership is the new VIP level of membership to our gyms, available to all our members in the Hounslow area. It comes with a range of exclusive benefits for only £20 a month more than standard membership.

Benefits include:
- free access to all classes (does not include yoga).
- a personal health plan, including one session with a personal trainer per week.
- free access to our online health and fitness course.
- two free tickets to our summer party.
- free parking at all our gyms, nationwide.

8 Read the email from your American friend Fiona. Write your reply to Fiona in about 100 words.

> **Exam tip**
> Check your work carefully after writing. Look for grammar, vocabulary and spelling errors, but also make sure you've included the four points in the question clearly.

From: Fiona
Subject: My visit

Hi!

I'm writing about my visit next month. I'm very excited to see you again!
What have you got planned for the first week? Are we going to visit anywhere outside your city? I've read about the shops in your city – they sound great. Are we going to go shopping? Finally, do you want me to bring anything from the US? If yes, let me know!

See you soon,
Fiona

Exam Time 3 Listening   Units 1–9

1 🔊 **ET1–9.1** Listen to Trish talking to Aidan about a family photo. Match people 1–5 with family words a–h. There are three extra family words.

NAME		RELATIONSHIP	
1	☐ Elsie	a	grandmother
2	☐ Nathan	b	mother
3	☐ Mia	c	cousin
4	☐ Jack	d	great-grandmother
5	☐ Ryan	e	father
		f	brother
		g	aunt
		h	stepmother

2 🔊 **ET1–9.2** Listen to a conversation with a girl who has just returned from a trip to France. Choose the correct answer.

1 Where did Debbie stay while she was in France?
   a a short distance from Paris
   b in the centre of the town
   c near a theme park
2 How did Debbie feel about her French language skills?
   a She wished she could speak as quickly as the French.
   b She was surprised at how much she could understand.
   c She thought she didn't speak well because of a limited vocabulary.
3 What does Debbie say about French food?
   a She enjoys it because it's unusual.
   b She could only eat some things her friend's mother cooked.
   c She would like to have tried more fish dishes.
4 Why didn't they go to an art exhibition?
   a It was outside and the weather was bad.
   b She'd seen the exhibition in London.
   c It wasn't open.
5 When is Debbie going to see her French friend again?
   a in autumn   b in spring
   c in two weeks
6 In the future Debbie wants to
   a become a teacher.
   b become a writer.
   c use French in her job.

3 🔊 **ET1–9.3** Listen to some information about Agatha Christie. Complete the notes with the missing information.

> **Exam tip**
> It's important to spell basic, easy words correctly, so check your spelling at the end.

Agatha Christie
- She was born in ¹*1890*.
- She wrote ² _____ detective novels.
- ³ _____ is the longest-running play in the world.
- She worked at a ⁴ _____ during the world wars.
- She worked with her husband in the ⁵ _____.
- Her books have sold over ⁶ _____ copies.

4 🔊 **ET1–9.4** Listen. Then listen again and write down what you hear during each pause.

> **Exam tip**
> If you miss a word, leave a space and continue. At the end, try to guess the missing word(s) from the context.

Exam Time 3 — Reading and Writing — Units 1–9

5 Complete the article with sentences a–h. There are three extra sentences that you do not need.

Exam tip
Use linking words to check if a sentence fits the surrounding text.

a One of the hardest things was writing essays.
b That was exactly what I expected.
c That way, they could experience what school life was like for teenagers at that time.
d I was amazed a week later when I received a letter saying that they wanted me to take part.
e That's because I've never been on TV before.
f That was really hard for me because I love chatting!
g I really enjoyed writing essays.
h But I loved learning how to make bread and cakes.

1950s School
by Bethany Jones

Last year I saw an advert in a history magazine asking for young people to take part in a reality TV show called *1950s School*. The idea was to take a group of young people and transport them back to a 1950s school. ¹___ I decided to put my name forward.

To apply, we had to write about ourselves and why we were interested in the show, and then have an interview with the programme's director. I was really excited, but I knew there were loads of people there and they only wanted fifteen. ²___

The lessons were very different to our lessons nowadays. The teachers were all really strict, and in lessons we had to just listen and take notes and not talk at all. ³___ In Physics, we learned about space, but not much was known at that time because this was ten years before people landed on the moon.

I found the homework quite boring. We just had to memorise a lot of facts. I really didn't enjoy that, but actually it's quite useful now because I can tell you all the capital cities of Europe! ⁴___ I usually use my laptop for writing and I'm quite fast at typing, but it took me ages to write everything by hand.

One good thing was the school meals. It was fun eating with all the others in the canteen, although the food wasn't brilliant! The best part of the whole experience for me was the cooking lessons. It was strange because only the girls learned cooking, while the boys practised making things out of wood. ⁵___ That's one thing from the past that I'll definitely do more of in the future!

6 Read the notice and answer the questions.

Exam tip
Only write the word or words that answer the question. If you write extra or unnecessary words, it will waste time.

1 How much do the classes cost? *nothing*
2 How did students describe the free English classes last year? ___
3 What levels are the classes? ___
4 What two things do you need to go to the classes? ___
5 How long will the free classes last? ___

Free English classes!

After the success of our free English classes last year, when you said that they were useful, there will be free classes for students at intermediate and elementary levels. The classes will be taught by trainee teachers (people learning to become teachers) on Mondays and Wednesdays from 6 p.m. to 8 p.m.

If you want to attend, please tell reception. You'll need to show your student ID and provide a telephone number where we can contact you.

The free classes will continue for two months. They are a great way to improve your English with extra practice, and you'll also help the trainees on our teaching course.

Exam Time 3 — Reading and Writing — Units 1–9

7 Read the story and answer the questions.

1 What's the population of Bangladesh?
   <u>over 160 million</u>
2 How much of the country is flooded during the rainy season? _____
3 What can't children usually do when the floods come? _____
4 How many children can go on each boat? _____
5 What else do students do besides lessons? _____

Bangladesh Boat Schools

With a population of over 160 million people, Bangladesh is one of the most crowded countries on Earth. It is also one of the most flooded countries. Every year, when the rainy season comes, up to seventy percent of the country is under water, and many small villages are cut off from the rest of the world. This means some children can't go to school on these days. But one local charity has a solution. Every morning, small boats travel along the river, picking up children. When they are full – they're big enough for around thirty children – they stop at the side of the river and start classes for the day. The children have Bengali, English, Maths and Science lessons. They also watch videos which help improve their general knowledge.

8 Read the article and complete the sentences. Use 1–3 words from the text in each gap.

1 Restorative justice was only recently added to the <u>formal justice system</u>.
2 In restorative justice, the criminal and the victim have _____.
3 The first aim of restorative justice is for the criminal and victim to _____.
4 In the meeting, everyone discusses how the criminal can _____.
5 Sometimes the criminal has to apologise or _____ to the victim.
6 Instead of just punishing the criminal, restorative justice tries to _____ the situation.
7 Sometimes restorative justice happens at _____ as other, more traditional punishments.

Restorative justice

Restorative justice in one form or another has been around for hundreds of years, but it's only in recent times that it's become part of the formal justice system. So what is it? Basically, it's a process where a criminal has a meeting with the victim of their crime, and sometimes other people in the area affected by the crime. So, for example, if someone robs someone in the street and they are later caught, a meeting is set up where the robber meets the victim and they talk about what happened.

There are three main aims of restorative justice. Firstly, the criminal and the victim can share their experiences. Secondly, the victim can explain exactly how they were affected and what damage has been caused to their lives. Finally, the criminal and victim (with the help of professionals) can discuss what the criminal can do to make things better. This might include paying the victim money, apologising and/or discussing what else the criminal can do.

Restorative justice is a form of punishment for crimes based on the idea of improving the situation rather than just punishing a criminal. However, it's often used at the same time as more traditional punishments such as prison time. For example, a criminal may get a shorter prison sentence if they agree to meet their victim(s).

9 Read the writing task and answer the questions. Then write your essay in about 100 words.

1 What type of essay do you need to write? _____
2 What three things do you need to include in your answer? _____

Write an opinion essay to answer this question: Are exams the best way to assess students? Include the following information:
- the advantages of exams.
- the disadvantages of exams.
- your own opinion.

Self-checks answer key

Unit 1 Self-check

Exercise 1
1 charging cable 2 take … selfie
3 upload 4 wireless earbuds 5 post
6 link 7 remote 8 follow 9 add … group
10 take … screenshot

Exercise 2
1 b 2 b 3 a 4 a 5 c

Exercise 3
1 twice 2 evening 3 minute 4 day
5 mealtimes

Exercise 4
1 'm/am chatting 2 don't often watch
3 lives 4 don't like 5 isn't/is not raining
6 Does … want 7 Are … doing

Exercise 5
1 being 2 to pay 3 to connect
4 to stay up 5 helping 6 to buy
7 to delete 8 going

Exercise 6
1 Shall 2 could 3 Why 4 not 5 how

Unit 2 Self-check

Exercise 1
1 sunny 2 gale 3 foggy 4 mild 5 boiling
6 degrees 7 flood 8 lightning

Exercise 2
1 strange 2 awesome 3 worried
4 absolutely 5 different 6 boring

Exercise 3
1 leaves 2 path 3 make 4 discovered
5 for 6 cave

Exercise 4
1 stayed 2 didn't see 3 took
4 didn't want 5 Did … have

Exercise 5
1 saw … was walking
2 were skiing … started
3 watched … were staying
4 was sitting … got
5 were watching … when

Exercise 6
1 Why did you do that … I didn't realise …
I thought   2 I didn't mean to … I see

Unit 3 Self-check

Exercise 1
1 garlic 2 pineapple 3 chillies
4 vinegar 5 ice cream 6 sauce

Exercise 2
1 healthy 2 Crunchy 3 creamy 4 juice
5 for 6 from 7 to 8 with

Exercise 3
1 a 2 b 3 c 4 c 5 a 6 b

Exercise 4
1 haven't ordered yet
2 Have you ever tried
3 have just finished
4 have never seen
5 Has it stopped
6 Have you ever cooked
7 has just won

Exercise 5
1 have visited 2 didn't go 3 enjoyed
4 has just opened 5 wrote … hasn't replied
6 have never had … tried

Exercise 6
1 I'll have
2 something to drink
3 Excuse me
4 your starter
5 you are

Unit 4 Self-check

Exercise 1
1 science fiction 2 cartoon 3 performance
4 character 5 hit 6 audience 7 action
8 episode

Exercise 2
1 stream 2 record 3 lyrics 4 playlist
5 along 6 performance

Exercise 3
1 holiday 2 family 3 dance 4 hat
5 party 6 music

Exercise 4
1 more popular than
2 were too
3 the tallest
4 as expensive as
5 the best play
6 old enough
7 better than
8 older than

Exercise 5
1 many 2 lots of 3 any 4 much
5 a few 6 little 7 some

Exercise 6
1 I'd rather … it sounds
2 would you prefer … I'd prefer … looks better

Unit 5 Self-check

Exercise 1
1 b 2 a 3 c 4 a 5 a 6 b 7 c 8 c

Exercise 2
1 warm down 2 coach 3 exercise
4 stretch 5 balance 6 programme

Exercise 3
1 supporters 2 defender 3 practice
4 score 5 player 6 manager

Exercise 4
1 opens 2 'll win 3 's going to score
4 'm going to take up 5 'm meeting
6 'll pay 7 're training

Exercise 5
1 'll get … do
2 don't practise … won't get
3 won't win … run
4 rains … 'll play
5 won't hurt … wear
6 'll arrive … is
7 won't be … go
8 buy … 'll swim

Exercise 6
1 up to … What about … don't know
2 got any plans … First

Unit 6 Self-check

Exercise 1
1 reservation 2 view 3 campsite
4 cruise 5 double 6 camp 7 sunglasses
8 torch 9 rent 10 facilities

Exercise 2
1 travel card 2 return ticket 3 traffic jams
4 single ticket 5 route

Exercise 3
1 trip 2 voyage 3 journeys 4 travel
5 excursion

Exercise 4
1 e 2 g 3 b 4 c 5 d 6 f 7 a

Exercise 5
1 S 2 S 3 D 4 D 5 S 6 S 7 D 8 D

Exercise 6
1 didn't catch … What I asked
2 first part … I said that
3 say that again

Unit 7 Self-check

Exercise 1
1 go 2 get 3 half-sister 4 same
5 have 6 common 7 gets 8 spending
9 stepmother

Exercise 2
1 strangers 2 best friend 3 mate
4 teammates 5 classmates

Exercise 3
1 a 2 f 3 e 4 b 5 c 6 d

Exercise 4
1 spent … would/'d get
2 would/'d go … was/were
3 had … would/'d travel
4 would/'d talk … was/were
5 would/'d do … lived
6 enjoyed … would/'d study
7 would/'d learn … had
8 knew … would/'d help

Exercise 5
1 who 2 where 3 who 4 that
5 which 6 who 7 where

Exercise 6
1 that boy 2 one do 3 one with
4 Which one 5 the back

Unit 8 Self-check

Exercise 1
1 shoplifter 2 fine 3 prison 4 vandal
5 theft 6 judge 7 clue 8 witness
9 pickpocketing 10 suspect

Exercise 2
1 uncomfortable 2 impossible 3 unkind
4 unfair 5 irresponsible

Exercise 3
1 fingerprints 2 criminals 3 witness
4 clues 5 area

Exercise 4
1 are used 2 was arrested 3 was found
4 are solved 5 wasn't seen 6 aren't sent
7 are given 8 Was … interviewed

Exercise 5
1 repaired 2 my hair cut 3 a pizza delivered
4 made 5 cleaned 6 stolen 7 taken

Exercise 6
1 wrong 2 fine 3 tell 4 that 5 see

Unit 9 Self-check

Exercise 1
1 critical 2 revise 3 confident 4 IT
5 general 6 teamwork 7 memorise
8 talented 9 speaking 10 presentation

Exercise 2
1 makes 2 make 3 made 4 take 5 take

Exercise 3
1 in 2 down 3 in 4 up 5 out

Exercise 4
1 was 2 said 3 gives 4 us 5 was
6 was writing 7 started

Exercise 5
1 Did you watch
2 Does he go
3 Have you finished
4 Why was Carrie
5 Who called
6 Who did you see
7 Who does
8 Why are you standing

Exercise 6
1 Where are 2 How long
3 Have you been 4 What are
5 Would you

Pearson Education Limited
KAO Two
KAO Park
Hockham Way
Harlow, Essex
CM17 9SR
England
and Associated Companies throughout the world.

pearsonenglish.com/widerworld2e

© Pearson Education Limited 2022

All rights reserved; no part of this publication may be reproduced, stored in a retrieval system, or transmitted in any form or by any means, electronic, mechanical, photocopying, recording, or otherwise without the prior written permission of the Publishers.

First published 2022

ISBN: 978-1-292-42279-4

Set in Frutiger Next Pro
Printed by L.E.G.O. S.p.A., Italy

Acknowledgements

The Publishers would like to thank all the teachers and students around the world who contributed to the development of Wider World Second Edition: Milena Aleksić, Tuğba Arslantaş, Gülşah Aslan, Mahgol Baboorian, Katarzyna Beliniak, Burcu Candan, Seri Diri, Hanna Dudich, Sema Karapinar, Nadiia Kasianchuk, Duygu Kayhan, Iryna Kharchenko, Ana Krstić, Ilknur Manav, Fulya Mertoğlu, Ivana Nikolov, Banu Oflas, Duygu Özer, Jagoda Popović, Marija Šanjević, Karmen Irizar Segurola, Elif Sevinç, Ludmila Shengel, Ayşe Sönmez, Anna Standish, Natalia Tkachenko, Pamela Van Bers, Jelena Vračar, Agnieszka Woźnicka, Münevver Yanık.

The Publishers would like to thank the following people who commented on the Wider World Second Edition content: Milena Aleksić, Mahgol Baboorian, Hanna Dudich, Izabela Kołando, Karmen Irizar Segurola, Joanna Srokosz, Anna Zając.

We would also like to thank the authors of the first edition of Wider World whose work has been the basis for creating this adaptation: Kathryn Alevizos, Carolyn Barraclough, Catherine Bright, Sheila Dignen, Lynda Edwards, Rod Fricker, Suzanne Gaynor, Bob Hastings, Jennifer Heath, Liz Kilbey, Stuart McKinlay, Sarah Thorpe, Tasia Vassilatou, Damian Williams, Sandy Zervas.

Photo Acknowledgements

123RF.com: Alexander Raths 29, Cathy Yeulet 51, 93, Chakrapong Worathat 36, David Cabrera Navarro 103, Elena Bochkova 27, Iakov Filimonov 75, ibrester 23, kazitsyn 6, Iosif Lucian Bolca 59, magone 27, maleeescape 96, Mariia Voloshina 27, milkos 31, 97, nan728 59, nejron 41, Nophamon Yanyapong 41, Olga Yastremska 7, 91, perig76 102, piksel 73, 73, Sean Pavone 19, Sergey Breev 68, serrnovik 49, tasch8790 19, travnikovstudio 61, Viacheslav Iakobchuk 77, Viacheslav Khmelnytskyi 59, Wattanaphob Kappago 6, Евгения Горенкова 28; **Getty Images:** Bettmann 108, BJI/Blue Jean Images 73, Chatcharin Sombutpinyo/EyeEm 6, Compassionate Eye Foundation/Steven Errico/DigitalVision 76, dowell/Moment 6, Image Source/Photodisc 81, Jose Luis Pelaez Inc 73, Kentaroo Tryman/Maskot 65, Maskot 87, piola666 20, skynesher/E+ 91, Thomas Northcut 73, Tony Anderson/DigitalVision 53; **Pearson Education Ltd:** 36, 68, 100, Gareth Boden 3, Jon Barlow 41; **Shutterstock:** 9, 39, 43, 93, 105, Africa Studio 97, antoniodiaz 11, bokan 41, DedMityay 27, gorillaimages 63, Gorodenkoff 83, Halfpoint 21, jonson 6, Kovankin Sergey 54, Maks Narodenko 27, maksimee 6, Marie-Claude Lemay 31, Miguel Garcia Saavedra 27, N Dove/20th Century Fox/Kobal 82, Phonlamai Photo 84, Sergiy Kuzmin 6, SurangaSL 59, Thomas Amby 13, Tim UR 27, tkemot 17, Viktar Malyshchyts 27, Wilson Webb/Columbia/Sony/Kobal 45

Illustrated by Laura Arias (Beehive Illlustration) 3,21,58,85,95,106; Tim Bradford (IllustrationX) 4,48,90,102,103; Michael Crampton 100l; David Cusik 68r; Gergely Fórizs (Beehive Illustration) 37,69,101; Chris Long 100r; Jamie Medlin 68l; Rupert Van Wyk 71,84; David Shephard 36

All other images © Pearson Education

Cover photo © Front: **Alamy Stock Photo:** Sara Winter